The New York Times

Understanding Autism

Esaïe Prickett, who has autism, tested an app using Google Glass, once a failed product, to help him learn to recognize emotions in others.
Page 58

The New York Times

Understanding Autism

At Aspiritech, a company with autistic employees, the "sensory break room" has fidget toys to help calm anxiety. Page 50

INTRODUCTION

Behold the Spectrum

Recognition of the broad possibilities for the autistic changed dramatically with the idea of the autism spectrum.

BY STEVE SILBERMAN

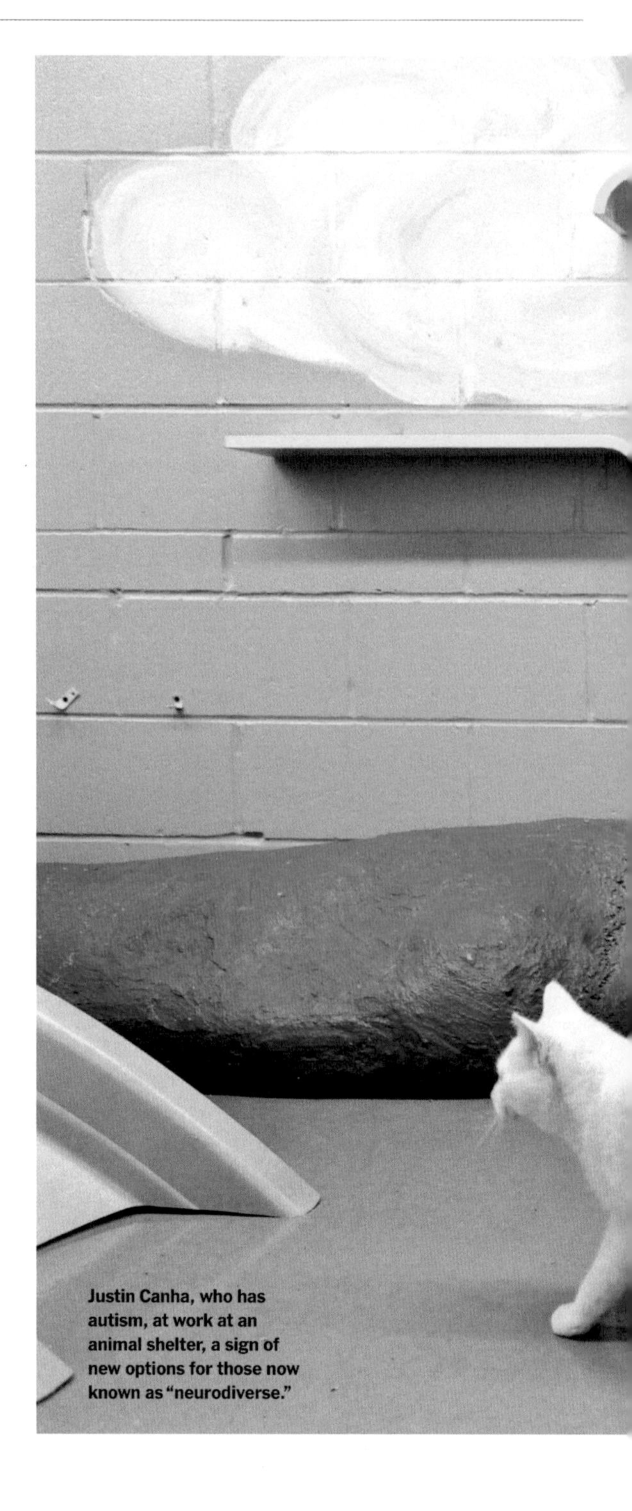

Justin Canha, who has autism, at work at an animal shelter, a sign of new options for those now known as "neurodiverse."

The endearingly awkward geek — bumbling through social interactions, impervious to subtle cues, meticulously pursuing his obsessions — has become a much-beloved figure in popular culture, particularly on TV. These characters' propensity for social clumsiness is redeemed by their having some uncanny depth of knowledge: think Abed Nadir's masterful command of TV trivia on "Community" or Shaun Murphy's photographic memory on "The Good Doctor." This trope has become so familiar that often the most obvious thing about these beguiling brainiacs need never be explicitly called out: They're autistic.

How times have changed. Just 30 years ago, the notion that the diagnosis of autism encompasses a diverse range of people with varying levels of cognitive ability and need for support — a "spectrum" — was still new to the psychiatric establishment. Introduced by the late British psychiatrist Lorna Wing and her colleague Judith Gould in the 1980s, the spectrum model of autism triggered major revisions in the bibles of psychiatry, the various iterations of the "Diagnostic and Statistical Manual of Mental Disorders" and the "International Classification of Diseases." Once these revisions went into effect, the floodgates for diagnoses opened wide, just as Gould and Wing — who was a psychiatrist as well as a mother, with a profoundly disabled daughter named Susie — intended.

Steve Silberman is the author of "NeuroTribes: The Legacy of Autism and the Future of Neurodiversity."

The effect on public perception of the formerly obscure condition was dramatic. Before the introduction of the spectrum model, representation was largely limited to the character of Raymond Babbitt in the 1988 movie "Rain Man": a wiz at such things as counting cards in poker and citing at a glance the number of fallen toothpicks, but unable to survive outside of a mental institution. Now the public faces of autism range from Julia on "Sesame Street," a Muppet who provides a relatable role model for autistic kids and their families, as Jennifer

Malia explores in her article "What a Muppet Means to My Family" (Page 78), to an actor with autism playing the role of an autistic boy, as profiled by Laura Collins-Hughes in "For This Actor, the World Really Is a Stage" (Page 74), to Time magazine's 2019 Person of the Year, Greta Thunberg, the 17-year-old from Sweden who launched a global movement of millions of young people to protest governmental indifference to climate change and who sailed across the Atlantic to bring her message to America.

The articles that follow chronicle the ongoing turbulence in the wake of that sea change. Societal and scientific perspectives are evolving so rapidly that the deep past of autism has become a strange and unfamiliar country. But we have much to learn from what we have left behind.

For most of the 20th century, the topic of autism was rarely broached in mainstream media, and then only as an unspeakable family tragedy (Eliot Fremont-Smith called autism "an illness, a suicide really, of the soul," in a Times book review in 1967). It barely rated as a footnote in most psychology textbooks, because it was considered to be so rare that most psychiatrists and pediatricians would likely never see a single patient. Indeed, the father of the diagnosis in the United States, Leo Kanner — a child psychiatrist at Johns Hopkins Hospital who wrote his first paper on the subject in 1943 — once estimated that he had seen only 150 "true cases" of autism in his career, after decades of evaluating children from all over the world.

Hardly anyone doubted him. The gruff, cigar-smoking clinician was so closely associated with the condition he claimed to have discovered, that autism was often referred to as "Kanner's syndrome."

But people on the spectrum have always been part of the human community, and Kanner was not the first to take note of them — the autism diagnosis simply had not yet been formulated. The 19th-century physician J. Langdon Down, who pioneered the study of developmental disabilities at the Earlswood Asylum in England, wrote about a boy who memorized "The Rise and Fall of the Roman Empire" and could recite it verbatim. (If he was interrupted, he'd start over from page one.) He also described other young patients who suddenly "lost wonted brightness" — including the ability to speak — in early childhood, seeming to suffer an abrupt "suspension of mental growth."

Tragically, Kanner theorized that the precipitating factor in autism is an emotionally frigid parent — the infamous 'refrigerator mother.'

Then in the 1920s, a Soviet psychiatrist named Grunya Sukhareva described a group of teenagers who had unusual sensory sensitivities, curiously focused interests, and an irresistible attraction to puns and wordplay. One of Sukhareva's patients taught himself all about the War of 1812 and loved to expound upon it. After the slightest interruption, however, he would have to deliver his lecture again from the beginning, like the young historian of Earlswood Asylum.

Five years before Kanner memorably described the condition in his landmark 1943 paper, a pediatrician at the University of Vienna named Hans Asperger gave a lecture in which he described a young man with unusually acute hearing who had the ability to pinpoint annoying flaws in other people with unnerving bluntness. Like Sukhareva's patients, the young man spoke with the vocabulary and syntax of a much older person, like a middle-aged pedant trapped in the body of a boy. In patients like this, Asperger saw reflections of stock figures from novels about bumbling aristocrats and jokes about absentminded professors.

It's important to remember that an estimated one in three people on the spectrum is also intellectually disabled, and the majority face far more daunting challenges in daily life than the quirky savants on TV. But the key insight of Asperger and his colleagues was to view the pedantic young man as a point on a continuum that also includes those who require nearly constant support.

Asperger would publish his own paper a year after Kanner's, in 1944. But it would remain an obscure footnote for decades, likely because by then the once-prestigious University of Vienna had been turned into a propaganda mill of racist pseudoscience by the Nazis, who prepared for the Final Solution against the Jews by practicing techniques of mass extermination on disabled children. Kanner gave the Viennese clinician only a single, dismissive mention late in his career once his own unassailable preeminence in the field was assured.

Translated into English for the first time in the late 1970s by Lorna Wing's husband, John, Asperger's overlooked paper became the primary inspiration for the spectrum model. Wing and Gould also introduced a new diagnosis — Asperger's syndrome — intended for teenagers and adults. But one fateful difference between Asperger's and Kanner's approaches was their belief in the prevalence of the conditions they described. "Once you learn to recognize the distinctive traits of autism," Asperger observed, "you see them everywhere" — which seems to be true today. But Kanner maintained, until he died in 1981, that his syndrome was exceptionally rare. This was, in large part, a self-fulfilling prophecy. By eliminating children with intellectual disability, epilepsy and co-occurring conditions like tuberous sclerosis (all of which are associated with autism) from consideration for a diagnosis, Kanner ensured that his precious syndrome would remain rare.

Further, instead of framing autism as a developmental disability that persists across the life span, Kanner classified it as a form of "childhood psychosis," and likely an ominous precursor to adult schizophrenia. This exclusive focus on children would have profound implications that are still felt today, as Eli Gottlieb grappled with in a New York Times Opinion piece published in 2015, "Adult, Autistic and Ignored" (Page 20). Most tragically, Kanner also theorized that the precipitating factor in autism is a self-centered, emotionally frigid, hyper-ambitious parent — the infamous "refrigerator mother."

The only hope for these children, experts agreed for most of the 20th century, was to be rescued from the allegedly toxic family environment by being placed in custodial care in a psychiatric institution, which had the collateral effect of rendering generations of autistic people invisible to society at large. (When the queen of potboilers, "Valley of the Dolls" author Jacqueline Susann, committed her autistic son Guy

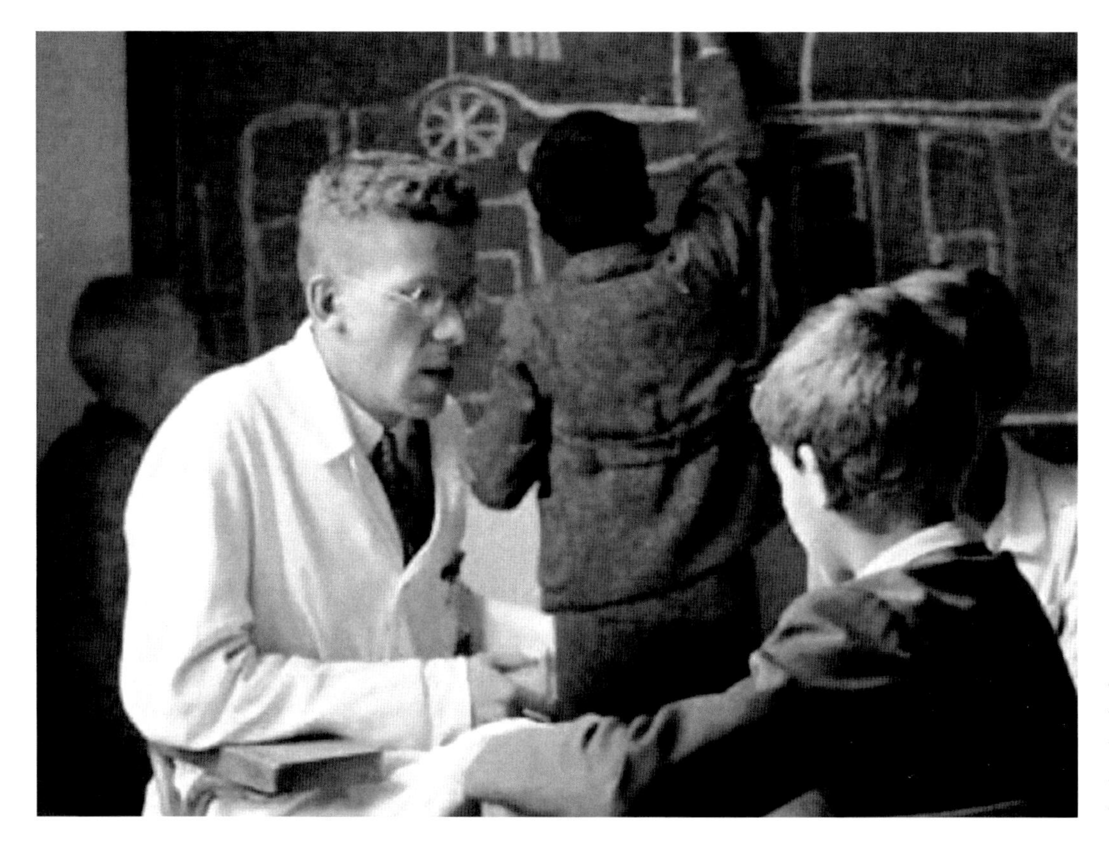

Though Dr. Hans Asperger was shadowed by his affiliation with the Nazis, his studies of boys in Vienna led to the notion of the spectrum.

to an institution, she and her husband sometimes told their friends they had shipped him to Arizona for his asthma.) As a result, when the number of new diagnoses started spiking in the 1990s after Wing and Gould's revisions went into effect, charlatans like the former gastroenterologist Andrew Wakefield, whose theories have been widely debunked, launched a propaganda war against vaccines that has ended up triggering deadly epidemics of easily preventable childhood diseases like measles and mumps worldwide.

Now we understand that virtually every one of the theories of autism that prevailed unchallenged for most of the 20th century was simply false, and wreaked tremendous damage on autistic people and their families. Autism is actually a common developmental disability, affecting one in 59 schoolchildren in the United States, according to the most recent estimate from the Centers for Disease Control and Prevention. That is in addition to a still-uncounted number of adults. Another long-held presumption — that autism affects four times as many men as women — is currently being reconsidered, as we learn that clinicians are heavily biased toward picking up signs of the condition in male children. And while some women may be better able to "mask" their autistic traits than men, the ability to do so comes at a great emotional cost.

We know this only because of another beneficial outcome of the broadening of autism into a spectrum that even Wing and Gould didn't anticipate: the long-delayed inclusion of autistic voices in public discussions of autism. Empowered by the internet, which alleviated the stress of awkward face-to-face interactions, adults on the spectrum began to share their experiences with one another, build their own communities and define themselves outside of the medical models of mental illness and disorder, as chronicled in a prescient 1997 article in The Times by Harvey Blume, who advocated the virtues of society learning to embrace what he called neurological pluralism. Shortened to the less cumbersome term "neurodiversity" by the Australian academic Judy Singer — whose bubbly and affectionate daughter never fit Kanner's narrow model — the term went viral, offering an alternative to the clinical language that had cast its pathologizing shadow on the lives of autistic people for decades.

Ultimately, the most valuable contribution of the spectrum model was to make visible a diverse population of people with enormous potential who had been exiled to the margins of society for a long time. The articles in this collection chronicle the efforts of parents, clinicians, researchers, teachers and disability-rights advocates to help autistic people to secure something they never seemed to have in the past: a promising future. ●

Child And Family

The autism spectrum is wide and encompasses people of all ages. Still, the lion's share of attention — research, therapy, theory, even literature — has gone to children with autism, and especially to boys with autism, in part because bias in identifying signs of the condition has led to claims that boys are four times more likely to be autistic than girls. This sometimes leaves on the edge of focus not only girls, but also autistic adults who, at age 21, often fall out of eligibility for many of the programs that may have helped them as children. Regardless of these inequities, what is nearly universally true is that any person with autism has a life-changing impact on his or her family, calling for new priorities, new sacrifices and, most of all, new understanding.

Jake, 10

To Some, the Subway Is Actually Soothing

It's loud, it's crowded, it's bright. But to the minds of autistic boys, it may be a paradise.

BY JOHN LELAND PHOTOGRAPHS BY TRAVIS HUGGETT

Justin, 7

Travis Huggett thought of the New York City subway as a means of getting from one place to another. Then he had a son on the autism spectrum.

To Orson, at age 8, a train was something more than transportation. It was soothing, endlessly fascinating, more intriguing than any destination it might reach. At his school for children with autism, other boys shared the same passion. When Huggett started photographing some of them, asking them about their interest in trains, he discovered the many different ways the children were drawn to them.

The original version of this article appeared on Nov. 8, 2018. It has been edited for clarity and length.

"Some were really interested in maps and timetables," Huggett said. Some liked model trains more than the real thing. Some found crowded cars too stimulating, but one wanted even more stimulation: His idea was to ride the subway to Coney Island and then ride the Cyclone roller coaster. "It was incredible how different they all are," he said. "I learned a lot about how diverse the community is."

At the New York Transit Museum, the staff noticed that their most enthusiastic visitors were boys on the spectrum, a phenomenon seen at similar museums around the globe. So in 2010 it created a Subway Sleuths program for autistic children in second to fifth grades that uses their common interest to help them develop social skills. Recently, it added

Orson, 8

Sean, 4

a pilot program for high school students. "Our purpose is all about communication and building friendships," said Regina Asborno, the museum's deputy director.

She said that even after years of running the program, the museum could not say why trains appealed to children on the spectrum, or why boys predominated. One explanation often heard is that trains' systemized nature — that they run on regular schedules along fixed routes — appeals to minds with autism.

But Huggett believes the diversity of children's interest defied such unified explanation.

"I don't think my son cares about that," he said. "He's not interested in maps and timetables. What they love about it isn't necessarily the same thing." Huggett said he tried to find girls who were as passionate about trains, but was unsuccessful.

When he took the portraits, he usually rode with both parent and child. They favored weekends because the crowds were smaller and less stimulating. Huggett preferred elevated trains because the light was better; none of the boys found the outdoor scenes too exciting.

Most objected to the noise, and covered their ears when a train pulled in. But few were intrigued by the photographer's presence, at least not compared to the draw of the trains.

"It's not often that you get to photograph people doing their favorite thing in the world," he said. "To have me along, taking pictures — they don't care." ●

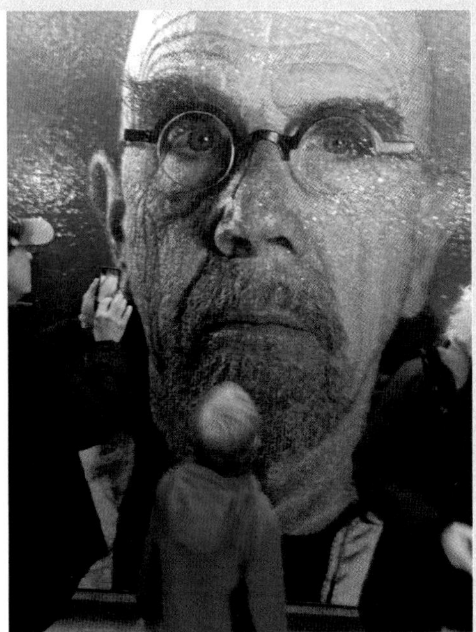

OPINION

For 'Train Kids,' The 2nd Avenue Subway Is a Dream Come True

BY KATHLEEN O'BRIEN

I had never asked my 6-year-old son about his dreams before, and he had never brought the subject up. But recently, his book of choice at bedtime, "Steam Train, Dream Train," gave me an opening.

"Dreams are the things you think about when you are sleeping," I explained. "What do you dream about?"

"Trains!" he answered. His voice was so confident, and his answer so fitting, that I was sure he understood me.

Not long after, as it happened, a train dream came true for New Yorkers. With great fanfare, the city unveiled a new stretch of the subway along Second Avenue, a project that took almost a century to bring into being. A spanking-new city subway line is also a big deal for "train kids" like mine. For many children affected by autism, like my son, trains can take on a mythic status, becoming a joy and a fixation. Trains may appeal to people on the autism spectrum because of the rapid visual stimulation they offer and the reliability and predictability of their routes and schedule; the toy versions also have spinning wheels that children with autism often love.

As soon as I could fit it in our schedule, we went to visit. As we descended the escalator to the new station, we were both excited. For my son, the chance to take a leisurely ride and check out escalators, elevators and trains brought pure bliss. He was laughing with delight.

A boy with autism, literally jumping with joy in a train station, can stand out in the crowd. A woman next to us smiled at my son's over-the-top antics. I explained that this was a fun excursion to see the new line and not our typical commute. She was a happy rider, too, but for prosaic reasons — her trip to her office was now much shorter.

We joined some tourists taking pictures of the art installed at the stations. It was better than a museum because I didn't have to worry about my son touching the displays. Should I have been worried about germs and dirt? Probably, but at least he was running his fingers along the newest, cleanest subway mosaics in the city.

He reached out in wonder at the image of a man and girl holding balloons, designed by the artist Vik Muniz. He and I stood next to the larger-than-life self-portrait of Chuck Close at 86th Street, examining the intricate mosaic tiles that create his beard. And I think he fell in love with Close's captivating portrait of the artist Sienna Shields.

I wouldn't be a New Yorker if I didn't have complaints about the subway. But the new subway line is glorious. Yes, it will probably raise rents. Yes, it took forever. But it is here. For the "train kid" in all of us, it's great to see.

The original version of this article appeared on Jan. 9, 2017. It has been edited for clarity and length.

The author's son checks out mosaics by Vik Muniz, left, and Chuck Close.

ESSAY

Mother and Daughter, Both With Autism

Autism spectrum disorder is wide in range and can affect families in a variety of ways. Genetics plays a key role, as this mother (and father) learned.

BY JENNIFER MALIA

"You convinced yourself that you and our daughter have autism," my husband yelled. "You did all this research and told the doctor what he needed to hear to diagnose you!"

"No, it wasn't like that," I said. "You know about all the testing we went through."

"I can't believe you brought her into this," he said. "You're like those mothers who make up medical problems about their kids. Why can't you just let her be a kid?"

"She's still the same girl she was before she got diagnosed," I said, tears dripping down my face. "And I'm still the same woman you married, too."

I knew then that if I couldn't persuade my husband of five years to accept my daughter's autism and my own, it would ruin our marriage and tear our family apart. Autism wasn't just a medical diagnosis; it was part of our identities. To reject our autism was to reject us.

Doctors originally told me my daughter had just a language delay. But I knew this couldn't explain the intensity of her emotional meltdowns. It took me hundreds of hours of medical research to understand that her difficulty socializing, repetitive routines, sensory issues and obsessive interests pointed to autism. I eventually realized that not only was she autistic — I was, too. A clinical psychologist diagnosed me and my daughter with autism spectrum disorder on the same day; she was 2 and I was 39.

A year later, when our then 2-year-old son was also diagnosed with autism spectrum disorder, my husband asked, "Do you think there's something wrong with everyone in our family?" As an autistic mother, I wasn't surprised to learn that I had another child on the spectrum. A 2014 study found that parents of autistic children are more likely to have elevated levels of autistic traits, whether or not these traits are enough to qualify for a clinical diagnosis of autism spectrum disorder.

In the study, when one parent scored high on a test that measures presence and severity of autistic traits (the SRS, or Social Responsiveness Scale), they were 52 percent more likely to have a diagnosed autistic child; when both parents scored high, they were 85 percent more likely to have one. Published early last year, the largest study ever conducted regarding genetic contributions to autism also found that inherited genes account for about 80 percent of autism risk.

But how was I supposed to parent our autistic children if my husband didn't even think they were autistic — and doubted my diagnosis too? It is not unusual for family members and others who know autistic women to have trouble accepting their autism diagnosis.

"Doctors, teachers and most people have a male stereo-

The original version of this article appeared on Oct. 15, 2019. It has been edited for clarity and length. Jennifer Malia is an associate professor of English at Norfolk State University and the author of the upcoming children's book "Too Sticky! Sensory Issues With Autism."

The author with her daughter Holly. A psychologist diagnosed the two with autism on the same day.

type of autism in mind; when they think of autism, they think of 'Rain Man,' not of a woman or girl," said Dr. Francesca Happé, a professor of cognitive neuroscience at King's College London. "For women who are married with children, this goes against several stereotypes people may hold about autism: male, single, few close relationships, no children."

The diagnostic criteria and assessment tools were developed primarily based on how autism presents in males, which means women can often be overlooked for an autism spectrum disorder diagnosis, depriving them of "an understanding of themselves as different, not damaged," said Dr. Lauren Kenworthy, a professor of neurology, pediatrics and psychiatry at the George Washington University School of Medicine and the director of the Center for Autism Spectrum Disorders at Children's National Hospital.

Sunyi Dean of Leeds, England, a mother of a 4-year-old nonverbal autistic son and a 7-year-old daughter who is on the waiting list for autism spectrum disorder diagnostic testing with the National Health Service, said that she worried about how her son will "relate to other people if he doesn't learn verbal communication, but at the moment he is happy in himself and settled into his special school."

With her home-schooled daughter, Dean said she was mostly ignored by professionals and other parents when she first raised concerns about autism, and now that she's being taken more seriously, the process has been "very difficult and slow."

As an autistic mother who was diagnosed after her son was, the biggest challenge for Dean has been finding time for self-care. "I always thought I wouldn't mind the demands of parenthood because I'm not hugely social and don't need to go out much," Dean said. "But . . . I still need a lot of personal space, a lot of downtime to recover on my own, and that's difficult to get with kids around."

By the time I received a diagnosis of autism, I was so overwhelmed by the responsibilities of working full time as an English professor while parenting three young children (a 1-year-old son and 2- and 3-year-old daughters) that I could barely keep it together.

The Malia family, near their home in North Carolina. From left, Nick, Jennifer, Noelle, Dave and Holly.

The year before my diagnosis, the stress of being an undiagnosed autistic mother nearly cost me my life. I spent two weeks in and out of the E.R. complaining of stroke-like symptoms while battling uncontrollable crying fits brought on by my desperate attempts to get medical treatment. "You need to learn to manage your pain. The E.R. is only for patients who actually have emergencies," a nurse said while handing me my discharge papers.

Though I didn't know it at the time, my crying fits at home and in the hospital were autistic meltdowns. I would find out many months later that what I had experienced was a cycle of sporadic hemiplegic migraines, which can lead to a coma or, in rare cases, even death. I often wonder if I would have been treated differently by medical staff if I had had an autism spectrum disorder diagnosis then, or if I still would have been dismissed as an anxious woman who didn't know how to manage her pain.

Research also suggests that undiagnosed autism has been harmful for women. In a 2016 study of 14 women, "many told us that the fact that their autism went unrecognized for so long had a very real and negative impact upon their mental health," said Dr. William Mandy, an associate professor in clinical psychology at University College London. "A lack of a diagnosis means a lack of appropriately targeted support, which can place an autistic individual under huge stress."

The published research on the experiences of autistic mothers is very limited. Two small qualitative studies in 2016 and 2017 consider pregnancy, childbirth and the postpartum period. The interviews of autistic mothers in these studies reveal challenges they had with sensory issues during breastfeeding and childbirth, and adapting to motherhood and infant care. Many said they felt unfairly judged by midwives and other caregivers on parenting skills and decisions.

Dr. Simon Baron-Cohen, a professor of developmental psychopathology and the director of the Autism Research Center at the University of Cambridge, and his colleagues have multiple studies underway to investigate the experience of autistic motherhood beyond the perinatal period. Presented at the 2016 International Meeting for Autism Research, their unpublished research involved an online survey of more than 300 autistic mothers. The study found the majority of them had extreme anxiety when talking to professionals about their children, encountered disbelief when they disclosed their diagnosis to professionals and struggled with daily parenting tasks.

"It should now be a routine requirement for autism researchers to collaborate with autistic people in every project," Dr. Baron-Cohen said. "Without the input of autistic mothers, we would have missed key issues" — such as the fact that autistic mothers have increased rates of postnatal depression and have been falsely accused of Munchausen syndrome by proxy on the assumption that they were making up their children's autism. He hopes this research will lead to more awareness of autistic motherhood experiences and the development of policy documents to improve the "woefully inadequate" services available for autistic mothers.

'Doctors, teachers and most people have a male stereotype of autism in mind; when they think of autism they think of "Rain Man," not of a woman or girl.'

"Many autistic women are highly attuned to their children," said Lana Grant, author of "From Here to Maternity: Pregnancy and Motherhood on the Autism Spectrum," a book aimed at helping autistic mothers with the challenges of pregnancy and motherhood. "They may see their child struggling with the same things that they struggled with as a child. They read up on everything they can about a behavior or condition and then they go to the professionals for help." Instead, they are seen as "too knowledgeable and hysterical," Grant said, and dismissed as trying to tell professionals how to do their job.

She was already the mother of five of her six children (three of whom are on the autism spectrum) when she got her autism diagnosis at 38. "Autistic mothers are their own worst critics," Grant said. She recommends that autistic mothers find a support network of other mothers on the spectrum, including those who are "out and proud" on social media, like her.

A few years after my diagnosis, my husband came to accept my own and our children's autism. I stopped lecturing him, realizing that he would eventually understand our differences on his own terms. He started going to therapy appointments with our children. Then last year, at our kids' taekwondo class, I told the father of another child that we are autistic. "I know," he said. "Your husband told me last time he was here."

My husband now respects my parenting decisions, knowing that I can help our children by drawing on my personal experiences living with autism. He is the supportive husband whom I married and a loving father who accepts our kids' differences.

While the limitations of my autism sometimes make it difficult for me to handle the demands of parenting three young kids, I am now more willing to seek help from support groups and therapists. Learning to understand and accept my own and my kids' autism was the best thing that ever happened to me, because it empowered me to be a better mom. ●

OPINION

Adult, Autistic And Ignored

After Eli became his 55-year-old brother's keeper, he learned how little aid is available for autistic adults.

BY ELI GOTTLIEB

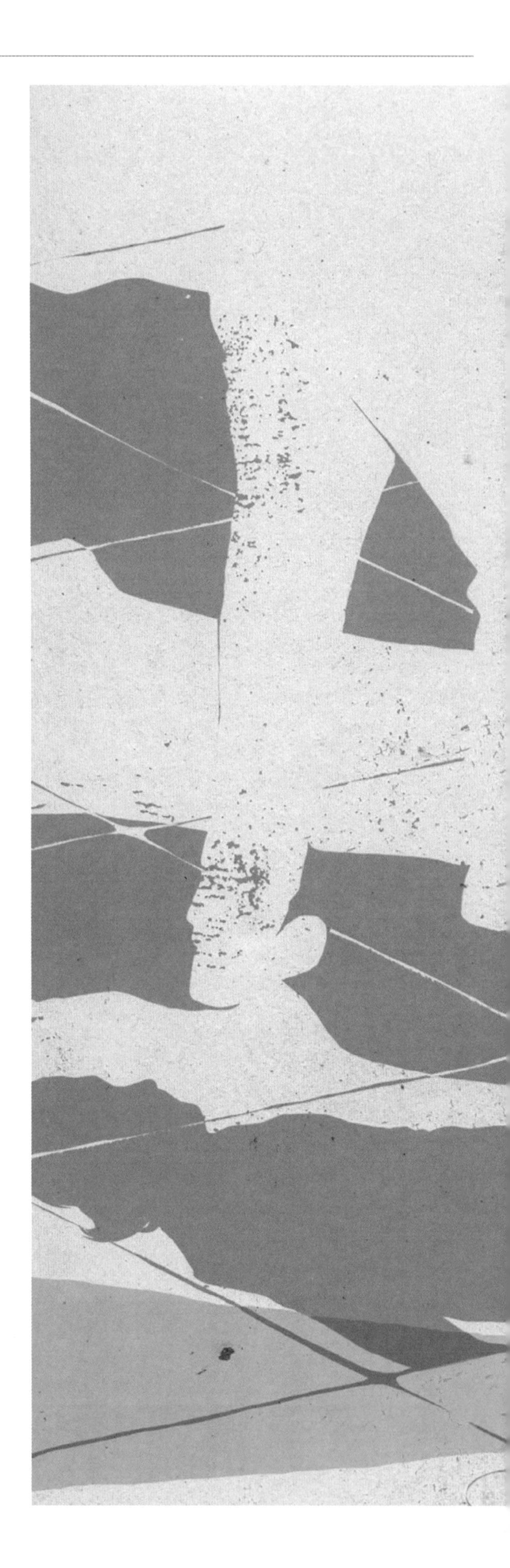

Two months before she died of pancreatic cancer in November 2010, my normally strong, stoical mother broke down weeping in my arms over the fate of my autistic older brother.

Institutionalized for over 40 years, Joshua, then 55, was in a stable situation and seemed relatively happy. But my mother was undone by that fear that haunts all parents of disabled children: *What will happen to them when I'm gone?* Though I hastened to assure her that I would become his guardian and watch over him after her death, she was inconsolable.

In reality, given the nature of the bond between them, I shouldn't have been surprised. As is often the case between mother and disabled child, the two early on formed a deep, exclusionary attachment that relegated the other members of our family to the outer boroughs of maternal attention. My brother's marathon tantrums, his gory public (and private) displays of self-mutilation and his regular physical assaults on our mother left me balancing as a boy on a narrow emotional catwalk between instinctual love for my sibling and blind rage. But none of that altered the depth of her feeling for him in the least. He was her main passion in life, and would remain so till the very end.

After her death, as promised, I signed the guardianship

The original version of this article appeared on Sept. 5, 2015. It has been edited for clarity and length. Eli Gottlieb is the author, most recently, of the novel "Best Boy."

papers and found myself suddenly a part-time resident in the island nation of adult autism in America. What I didn't realize at the time was just how uncharted the waters around that island would turn out to be.

I knew plenty about childhood autism, of course. A vast autism infrastructure has grown up around these children, with an array of new schools, websites, activist organizations, support and advocacy social networks, and eloquent voices at the very highest cultural and political levels of our society speaking of the rights of those with autism. And the lumping of the Asperger's syndrome diagnosis and a variety of related childhood disorders under the rubric of autism spectrum disorder, or A.S.D., has produced "sufferers" of autism so high-functioning they often regard their autism as a gift or visionary complement to life. This aggregate "big tent" approach to autism also partly explains the rise in the sheer numbers of children given that diagnosis.

But children eventually grow up. Roughly 500,000 children with autism will become adults over the next 10 years, and as they step through the door of age 21, they'll find themselves inheritors of a sad paradox. The variety of federally mandated supports and services available to them until then will have expired; the source of their funding will switch to the far smaller pie of state-by-state money. These resources, along with Medicaid and Social Security, are more fragmented and difficult for families to navigate. So the financial support — used to train them for jobs, find housing, obtain therapy — will dwindle at the exact moment in time they need it most. Unemployment among adults with autism — most of them higher functioning than my brother — is common. An estimated 90 percent of adults with autism are unemployed or underemployed.

When individuals with autism step through the door of age 21, they'll find themselves inheritors of a sad paradox — financial support will dwindle at the exact moment in time they need it most.

State funding, it seems, remains keyed to the idea that the same maturational curve applies both to "neurotypicals" and those with disabilities, and apparently relies on a magical-thinking belief that these young adults will somehow smoothly make the transition into adulthood without special guidance. Some states now get matching federal funds, but the steep drop-off — and the steep challenge for parents and children — remains.

It's part of a larger disconnect. There is little current substantive national discussion on the fate of middle-aged or elderly autistic people like my brother, who are living in therapeutic communities, or with their aged parents or in group homes, or sometimes undiagnosed in mental hospitals. Little research money is spent on members of this demographic, and there is almost no public policy debate on how best to serve them. Not much is known of the particular health problems linked to their long-term care, or how their autism progresses and changes over time. As Dr. Joseph Piven, a professor of psychiatry, pediatrics and psychology at the University of North Carolina at Chapel Hill, has put it, "There is almost no literature on older adults with autism in the field, so we have virtually no knowledge base."

Joshua is fortunate. As the beneficiary of decades of the hard-working advocacy of my mother, he now resides in the social and medical equivalent of a perfect fit — a beautiful, well-staffed therapeutic community in central New Jersey. Retired from active daily work after a long career of doing things like busing tables at McDonald's (too difficult); serving in a high school cafeteria (same) and working on the lawn crew of the large "farmstead" — a rural therapeutic community — where he spent many years (a job he loathed but tackled with a certain grim tenacity), he was moved at age 57 from the main campus to another a few miles away, designed specifically for older residents.

But even this place grapples with the stark realities. I regularly receive terse calls from my brother announcing the departure of a care worker he'd grown attached to. Why? Because therapeutic communities and "congregate settings" for adults with autism suffer from dramatic job turnover. Direct care staff are the true unsung heroes of the mental health universe, providing the stability and warmth of family when family is gone or far away. But poor pay virtually guarantees high turnover.

In terms of overall expenditure, government support for people with autism is considerable. The Combating Autism Act was passed under President George W. Bush in 2006 and authorized generous outlays for screening, early intervention, education and research. It was renewed in 2014 (its name was changed to the more palatable Autism Cares Act) under President Obama. But a quick glance at the funding priorities shows little devoted to people my brother's age.

While more funds would help, it's not enough to throw money at adult autism. What's needed instead is an intelligent, directed deployment of resources and a larger seat at the table of policy debate at both state and federal levels.

Karen Parenti, the vice president of community solutions for Bancroft, the service provider which owns and oversees my brother's residence, noted an urgent need for things like longitudinal studies on the long-term effects of medications used in autism care and financial support for lifelong learning programs and public education. To Louis F. Reichardt, the director of the Simons Foundation Autism Research Initiative, distinguishing the needs of adults with autism from

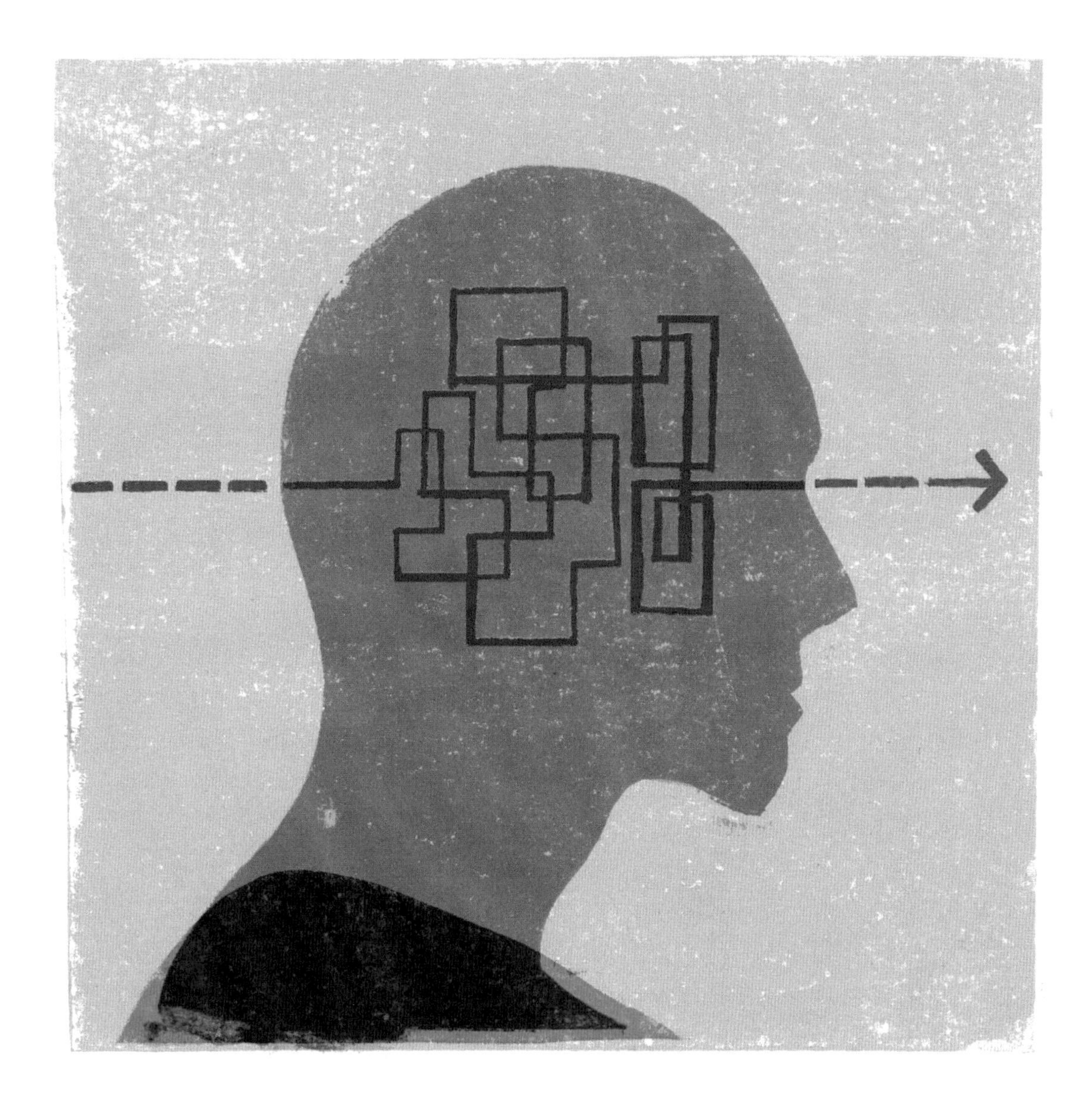

those of the younger population is paramount: We need to "identify what features these adults share or do not share with the pre-adult population, such as I.Q., verbal ability and social skills. This might tell us to what extent maturity and aging influence the severity of the deficits associated with autism," he wrote in an email.

In truth, what's simply needed is more of everything. But none of it will arrive in time to have an impact on the life of my brother.

On a recent visit to Joshua at his facility, the drill was the same as ever. My girlfriend and I greeted the affable staffers, and then took him out for a meal, where he defaulted to the same cycling, anxiety-fueled series of questions he does every time we're together: "I've come a long way, haven't I?" Or "Are you happy I'm doing as well as I am while seeing you?" Or, repeatedly, "What time do I have to return home tomorrow?" We saw a movie in blessed conversational silence, stayed overnight in a hotel with him, in that way fulfilling his dream of getting off campus for at least a night, and the next day bid him a heartfelt goodbye.

When I was younger, these visits would shatter me, and I'd often drive home in tears. But such extremities of feeling are long behind me. I'm soothed by the thought that he seems reconciled with his destiny. It's reassuring to know that my brother will continue to live out his life as he has for the last many years, his mind stabilized by powerful medications, his thoughts revolving around his next activity and meal, the legacy of my mother's work visible in his neat, sunny room and sparkling surroundings.

Is ignorance a blessing? In certain circumstances, yes. Among the many things he'll be unaware of, blessedly, is just how lucky he is. ●

ESSAY

Reluctant Keepers

We have always believed that our twins should take responsibility for their older brother when we no longer can. Are we asking too much of them?

BY ELIZABETH CHOI

Grace will get the pearls passed down from my grandmother. Her twin brother, Nick, will get the woodworking tools my husband, Dan, inherited from his grandfather. They will also inherit their brother, Jeffrey.

Jeffrey was 3 when his idiosyncrasies — his fascination with spinning objects, his sensitivity to the hum of fluorescent lighting — became symptoms leading to a diagnosis. I was pregnant with the twins when the pediatrician leaned forward, eyes intent on mine, and said: "I want you to understand, there is no cure for autism. Jeffrey will need care for the rest of his life."

Firstborns are often frustrated by the disruptions caused by a new sibling, but to an autistic child who craves structure and is sensitive to light and noise, the addition of two squalling infants is a catastrophe.

Jeffrey's frustration developed into tics, like fluttering his fingers in front of his eyes. He became increasingly hyperactive and angry, sometimes even dangerous: I once caught him pressing his hands against Grace's face in an attempt to muffle the shrill sound of her crying. When the twins started crawling, Jeffrey kicked them if they got too close to his toys arranged on the floor in a pattern known only to him.

At night, Dan and I lay in bed, two 20-somethings debating ethics in whispers while our children slept. Where does compassion for Jeffrey's disabilities end and Nick and Grace's rights to a safe and normal childhood begin?

Eventually, Nick and Grace grew old enough to protect themselves, but they were still too young to understand Jeffrey's disabilities. At 8, Jeffrey still liked the sensation of chewing on hard objects and gnawed the critical piece in Nick's latest Lego structure and the arm of Grace's favorite doll.

The twins saw Jeffrey as a Godzilla-like monster rampaging through their young lives and I struggled to point out Jeffrey's strengths. Unlike many children with autism, Jeffrey was affectionate and gave us hugs with his trademark intensity. And there were moments when he seemed like any other kid. Once when he ran into the kitchen asking for a snack, I tried to coax out his manners by saying, "What do you say? It starts with a P, ends with E?" "Hmm . . ." Jeffrey said, hand on his chin, sly smile on his face, "Plate?"

By the time Nick and Grace were teenagers, their older brother was mostly an embarrassment who shouted inappropriate comments during school performances. Once Jeffrey became interested in girls, he crashed Grace's slumber parties and tried to impress her friends by following them around while reciting the distances between planets.

When Grace complained that Jeffrey was giving her friends inappropriately long hugs, I had to concede that there needed to be a shift in the point where Jeffrey's rights ended and Nick and Grace's rights began. We started confining Jeffrey to his room when the twins had friends over, albeit guiltily, plying Jeffrey with treats to lessen the sting.

When Grace complained that Jeffrey was giving her friends inappropriately long hugs, I had to concede that there needed to be a shift in where Jeffrey's rights ended and his siblings' began.

Nick and Grace were 15 when Jeffrey graduated from high school and began the difficult transition from the sheltered special education system to the unmerciful adult world.

We have always believed that Nick and Grace should take responsibility for their brother when we no longer can. We have worked to engrave that duty on their hearts, but they accept it grudgingly. I wonder if we failed as parents to instill compassion in the twins, if we somehow hardened their hearts instead of softening them. Dan reminds me that few people accept familial duty with joy.

We have worked to make the twins' burden as light as possible. We placed Jeffrey in one of the rare independent living communities for disabled adults, where he lives in an apartment with a roommate, manages his own shopping and cooking, and has friends. He says he is happy there.

But we still pay several hundred dollars each month to cover the community's fee for having an on-site resident assistant, as well as Jeffrey's clothing, transportation and other personal expenses. It is likely that Nick and Grace will need to carefully ration our life insurance payout to keep their brother clothed, fed and supervised.

Nick and Grace, meanwhile, are now busy young adults with romantic relationships and promising careers. They rarely ask after their brother, but when we all get together for holidays, they treat Jeffrey with detached kindness rather than the resentment of the past. We sometimes remind the twins of their duty to care for Jeffrey, and with the optimism and confidence of youth, they say they will handle it, and anyway, it is far in the future. But I know that the future has a tendency to arrive sooner than expected, and that it will not be easy.

Are we asking too much of the twins? What is the responsibility of a sibling for a sibling? When we are both gone, the burden will be passed down, along with the silverware and the photo albums. Nick and Grace will be forced to take up where we left off. And we can only hope that we have done right by all of our children. ●

The original version of this article appeared on May 25, 2018. It has been edited for clarity and length. Elizabeth Choi is a freelance writer in Maine.

Visualizing Life With Autism

A photographer set out to learn more about her autistic brother by taking pictures of him. The project blossomed when he became a collaborator.

TEXT BY SARA ARIDI

PHOTOGRAPHS BY ERIN LEFEVRE

Growing up, Erin Lefevre realized that her younger brother, Liam, was "a little bit different from everyone else." He was in and out of doctors' offices as an infant. At 3 years old, he was told he was on the autism spectrum.

Lefevre had a hard time articulating her brother's condition when she was a child. But today she is perfectly comfortable raising the issue. So much so that she has been sharing intimate moments from Liam's everyday life through her documentary project "Liam's World."

"I wanted to better understand how he sees the world and get a better sense of who he is as a person transitioning from youth into adulthood," she said.

Lefevre, seven years older than Liam, started shooting him in 2014, when her brother was 14. When she started sharing photos of Liam with her peers and editors, she would often face stereotypical notions of what mental health conditions "look like."

"A common response was: 'It doesn't look like there's anything wrong with him,'" Lefevre said. "I just really wanted to emphasize that mental health isn't about how someone looks. It's a state of mind."

Photographing a state of mind would prove difficult. How can one visualize a disorder associated with impaired communication, social skills and repetitive behaviors? After giving it some thought, Lefevre asked Liam to write down an observation or memory alongside each photo to explain how he felt in the moment.

By allowing Liam to share his thoughts, the photo essay captures the complexity of the autism spectrum disorder. Liam's disability affects some of his intellectual capabilities. But it doesn't define his personality. "In a lot of ways, he's just like any other teenager," Lefevre said. "He likes to push buttons sometimes. He can be a bit cheeky."

The project has helped Lefevre better understand her brother, and it has also allowed him to reflect on his own questions and insecurities. When Lefevre posted some of the images on social media, Liam was a bit hesitant about having his life laid bare. He once sent his sister a text message saying, "I can be a little ashamed sometimes that I have autism." Those worries led to long, constructive conversations. She told Liam that adding his insight could enlighten others and show that his condition is just one aspect of his identity.

Now Liam is more at ease with the work, and Lefevre herself feels more confident in sharing it after having Liam contribute. He's no longer just a subject; he's also a collaborator.

Lefevre hopes other families who have relatives with special needs can "see pieces of themselves" in the images. And regardless of which direction her career takes, she says she is determined to document her brother's story for as long as possible. "It's a project that I think can go on for essentially his entire life." ●

The original version of this article appeared on Aug. 22, 2018. It has been edited for clarity and length.

I feel relaxed when I play with string

I was paying attention and making eye contact

I was on a huge rock in central park.
I wasn't afraid at all.

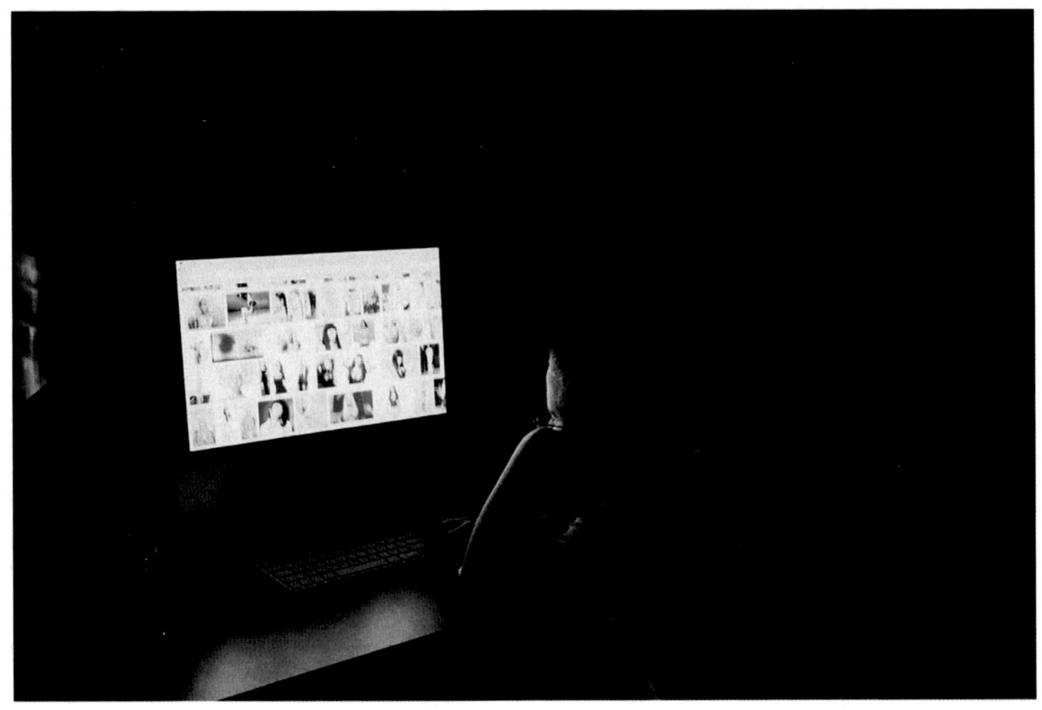

I like celebrities who are girls
because they're beautiful

I don't take the train alone yet but I'm learning as much as I can.

Tyree and I go to school together and we always like to laugh and joke around. He's my best friend.

I felt happy when I release the balloon.

When the rain started to come down
I was ok with it

my mom and I like watching tv together in the livingroom

I love my dog molly because I had her for a very long time.

Autism And Science

While huge strides have been made in understanding the psychology of the autistic mind, we still know very little about what causes autism. But the wheels of research, fueled by the increasing frequency of diagnoses, are spinning ever faster in labs around the country. Experts say that the earlier a diagnosis can be made in a child, the better the chances that therapy will help. Thus, great effort has been spent trying to identify the gene or genes responsible for autism. At the same time, medical researchers are looking inside the brain for additional clues to managing autism.

For This Actor, The World Really Is a Stage

In 'The Curious Incident of the Dog in the Night-Time,' the lead actor, himself autistic, played the role with authenticity.

BY LAURA COLLINS-HUGHES

The Search for A Biomarker for Early Diagnosis

The sooner autism is diagnosed and a child begins therapy, the better the outlook. A study of children's responses to hearing their names offers new clues.

BY PERRI KLASS, M.D.

Every pediatrician knows that it's important to diagnose autism when a child is as young as possible, because when younger children get help and intensive therapy, their developmental outcomes improve, as measured in everything from improved language, cognition and social skills to normalized brain activity.

"The signs and symptoms for most children are there between 12 and 24 months," said Dr. Paul S. Carbone, an associate professor of pediatrics at the University of Utah and a co-author of "Autism Spectrum Disorder: What Every Parent Needs to Know," published by the American Academy of Pediatrics. "If we can get them in for evaluation by then, the therapies are available as young as those ages, you can easily start by 2," he said. "We'd like to give kids the benefit of getting started early."

That means taking parents seriously when they bring up concerns about what they regard as strange behaviors and interactions on the part of babies and toddlers, and it also means that we try to screen all our patients, often with a checklist for parents to complete, like the Modified Checklist for Autism in Toddlers, or M-CHAT. Children whose scores indicate a concern are then supposed to be referred for a full developmental assessment. The Centers for Disease Control and Prevention's website lists developmental milestones to look for; missing them may be an early sign of autism.

So we all know this is important. We also know that we are not, collectively, doing a very good job of screening all children, that the questionnaires often over-identify children who don't actually need full assessments, and that the referral process can be plagued with long waits (and when a young child has to wait months for the assessment, that works against the benefit of early diagnosis). Children in minority groups are diagnosed at an older average age than white children, and therefore get therapy later, contributing to increased disparities.

"We're trying to develop methods that might add more precision," said Dr. Geraldine Dawson, a professor of psychiatry and behavioral sciences at Duke University, and the director of the Duke Center for Autism and Brain Development.

Autism is by its nature a social communication disorder, Dr. Carbone said, and two relatively specific early signs are failing to look at a person who calls your name and not manifesting what is called joint attention. As early as 9 months, and reliably by 18 months, a neurodevelopmentally typical

---

The original version of this article appeared on April 22, 2019. It has been edited for clarity and length.

Children with autism took significantly longer to look away from a video after hearing their name called.

child will look back and forth between an object of interest and a caregiver, attempting to create a mutual experience; a child on the autism spectrum is less likely to do this.

Researchers looking to find a biomarker that may help with the early diagnosis of autism have seized on the question of how young children react to hearing their names called. Dr. Dawson was the corresponding author on a study in April 2019 in the journal Autism that used computer vision analysis to look at the reactions of toddlers from 16 to 31 months old, in response to hearing their names called. Those with autism spectrum disorder took significantly longer to look away from a video and orient toward the person who had called.

"Toddlers and infants who will go on to develop autism are paying attention to the world in a very different way," Dr. Dawson said.

The hope is that eventually a tool can be made that would be easily available in low-resource countries or, for that matter, in any area in the United States, perhaps by having

parents collect data on their phones. "It's very important to screen for autism early," Dr. Dawson said. "We have research that suggests that parents are quite good at noting that a child is not behaving normally, and it's important to get children diagnoses."

The gold standard for diagnosis is to have the child evaluated by experts in behavior and development. Dr. Susan Levy, a developmental pediatrician at the Center for Autism Research at the Children's Hospital of Philadelphia, said, "Right now, unfortunately the average age of diagnosis according to the C.D.C. is around 4 or a little bit older. The hope is to get it closer to 2." Diagnosis is currently made clinically, after a family has waited out what can be a long time on a waiting list.

"Diagnosis is made by a really good history of what the child's development has been like in the different streams of development, language, motor," she said. The specialist also observes the child directly: "We look closely at social skills, at how they respond to their name, are they using eye contact to find out about others' thoughts, are they using language to communicate, do they have any repetitive or unusual behaviors?"

'Right now, unfortunately the average age of diagnosis according to the C.D.C. is around 4 or a little bit older. The hope is to get it closer to 2.'

The assessment also needs to look carefully at any repetitive behaviors, she said, and ideally may involve a team of specially trained observers with expertise in speech and language and occupational therapy.

And then, for children whose development and behavior are concerning, there need to be complex conversations with the parents. "We talk about where their skills are now, how their development may differ, what makes it harder for them," Dr. Levy said. "About what their strengths and weaknesses are and what characteristics they have that are consistent with the criteria for having an autism spectrum disorder."

The younger they are, she said, the more challenging it is to predict what their trajectories may be, although, of course, the younger they are, the greater the hope of changing those trajectories for the better. And that will mean that the family needs to establish a strong relationship with the people who will work with the child.

"It's not a sprint, it's a marathon or a triathlon," Dr. Levy said. "It's important to find providers you're comfortable with, who are not promising quick fixes — there are no quick fixes for a family with a diagnosis of autism." ●

Mapping the Brain's Genetic Landscape

BY BENEDICT CAREY

For the past two decades, scientists have been exploring the genetics of autism, schizophrenia and other brain disorders, looking for a path toward causation. If the biological roots of such ailments could be identified, treatments might follow, or at least tests that could reveal a person's risk level.

In the 1990s, researchers focused on genes that might possibly be responsible for mental distress, but then hit a wall. Choosing so-called candidate genes up front proved to be fruitless. In the 2000s, using new techniques to sample the entire genome, scientists hit many walls: Hundreds of common gene variants seemed to contribute some risk, but no subset stood out.

Even considered together, all of those potential contributing genes — some 360 have been identified for schizophrenia — offered nothing close to a test for added risk. The inherited predisposition was real; but the intricate mechanisms by which all those genes somehow led to symptoms such as psychosis or mania were a complete mystery.

Now, using more advanced tools, brain scientists have begun to fill out the picture. In a series of 11 papers, published in Science and related journals, a consortium of researchers has produced the most richly detailed model of the brain's genetic landscape to date, one that incorporates not only genes but also gene regulators, cellular data and developmental information across the human life span.

The $50 million project, initiated in 2015 and financed by the National Institute of Mental Health, involves more than a dozen research centers and scores of specialists in cell biology, genetics and bioinformatics, the application of advanced computer learning to huge data sets. It is an all-hands, brute-force effort, coordinating top brain banks and brain scientists at major research centers.

The original version of this article appeared on Dec. 13, 2018. It has been edited for clarity and length.

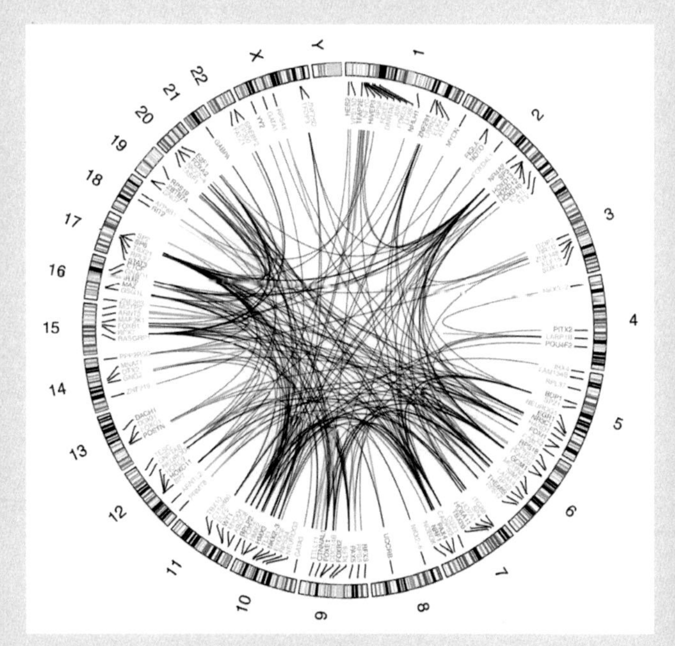

Left: A visualization of the gene regulatory network in a specific brain cell. The outer numbers and letters indicate chromosomes, and the small blue letters indicate genes active in this type of cell. Right: Magnetic resonance imaging scans of a healthy brain.

The new model was based in part on analyses of nearly 2,000 human brains, from people with and without diagnoses, collected over decades. In one of the papers, a research team led by Dr. Mark Gerstein, a professor of bioinformatics at Yale University School of Medicine, began by combining all those genes, as a group, and calculating the combined added risk they impart into a single coefficient. That calculation on its own barely beats a random guess in assessing added risk.

Dr. Gerstein and his team then integrated those implicated genetic locations with other biological data: Patterns of gene expression from single cells. The varying ratios of different cell types, in different individuals. The activity of transcribing and regulating molecules, which moderate the expression of genes — the conversion into functioning proteins — over time. This combined analysis improved predictive power to about 25 percent over random guessing, from 4 percent in previous models.

"One of the things that's really interesting about psychiatric disease is that it's more heritable than many other diseases," Dr. Gerstein said. "But people don't have any clue about mechanisms between the underlying gene variants" and the symptoms, for disorders such as schizophrenia or autism. "Now, we're starting to fill that in."

In another report, a research team led by Dr. Nenad Sestan, another brain scientist at Yale, analyzed cells from tissue samples from 16 locations in the brains of dozens of people of all ages. The brains were collected post-mortem, and about half were from people who had been diagnosed with a disorder.

The team tracked changes in the activity of genes and other molecular processes in those cells, looking for patterns that correlated with autism, schizophrenia or bipolar disorder. It identified a network of genes active in specific cell types — genes that were apparently communicating with one another — at about the stage in life when disorders begin to surface.

The result from all this work is a computer model for brain genomics that scientists can search — a database that charts specific genetic addresses in the brain and reveals which genetic and biological processes are active there, and at what point during maturation.

Dr. Matthew State, chair of the department of psychiatry at the University of California, San Francisco, and a co-author on two of the papers, said: "Essentially what these papers do is lay out cellular and molecular landscape at a resolution that's never existed before. I see it as foundational work, and an investment that will pay off in giving us a far richer context to develop new hypotheses and study these disorders."

How Twins Look At Faces May Offer Insight Into Autism

A study of toddlers (some autistic, some not) suggests important genetic differences. Will it lead to understanding how specific genes relate to autism?

BY PAM BELLUCK

The genes in identical twins are 100 percent the same, which is useful in conducting genetic research.

How we look at other people's faces is strongly influenced by our genes, scientists have found in research that may be especially important for understanding autism because it suggests that people are born with neurological differences that affect how they develop socially.

The study, published in the journal Nature, adds new pieces to the nature-versus-nurture puzzle, suggesting that genetics underlie how children seek out formative social experiences like making eye contact or observing facial expressions. Experts said the study may also provide a road map for scientists searching for genes linked to autism.

"These are very convincing findings, novel findings," said Charles A. Nelson III, a professor of pediatrics and neuroscience at Harvard Medical School and Boston Children's Hospital, who was not involved in the research. "They seem to suggest that there's a genetic underpinning that leads to different patterns of brain development, that leads some kids to develop autism."

Dr. Nelson, an expert in child development and autism who was an independent reviewer of the Nature study, said that while autism is known to have a genetic basis, how specific genes influence autism's development remains undetermined.

The study provides data on how children look at faces, including which features they focus on and when they move their eyes from one place to another. The information, Dr. Nelson said, could help scientists "work out the circuitry that controls these eye movements, and then we ought to be able to work out which genes are being expressed in that circuit."

"That would be a big advance in autism," he said.

In the study, scientists tracked the eye movements of 338 toddlers while they watched videos of motherly women as well as of children playing in a day care center. The toddlers, 18 months to 24 months old, included 250 children who were developing normally (41 pairs of identical twins, 42 pairs of nonidentical twins and 84 children unrelated to each other). There were also 88 children with autism.

Scientists study identical twins because 100 percent of their genes are the same, so if they share characteristics that are more individualized in other children, those traits are considered at least partly inherited. Nonidentical or fraternal twins share 50 percent of their DNA, so stark differences between identical and nonidentical twins suggest that those traits are strongly influenced by genes.

In the study, how much one identical twin looked at the eyes of people on screen matched the other identical twin 91 percent of the time. For fraternal twins, the match dropped to 35 percent. For unrelated children, when measured as pairs of the same age and sex, the match was 16 percent. And when the unrelated children were paired at random, their time spent looking at eyes did not match at all, said Warren Jones, the study's senior author and an assistant professor of pediatrics at Emory University School of Medicine.

The original version of this article appeared on July 12, 2017. It has been edited for clarity and length.

The study shows that a social behavior significantly different in children with autism is strongly influenced by genetics.

How much the children looked at mouths followed a similar pattern. And although each toddler watched the videos without other children present, identical twins often moved their eyes at nearly the same moment — as close as 16.7 milliseconds apart — and in the same direction.

"It's a really remarkable set of findings in that it really shows that genetic factors are driving differences in the way that toddlers are looking at faces," said Dr. Brad Duchaine, a professor of psychological and brain sciences at Dartmouth, who was not involved in the study. "This suggests that genetic differences drive this important aspect of the way that we interact with others."

With the children with autism, the researchers found that, compared with typically developing toddlers, they spent significantly less time looking at faces and more time looking at objects. The difference was so consistent that researchers could identify most children with autism just by looking at the eye-tracking results, Dr. Jones said. That result reinforced the team's previous research showing that babies from 2 months to 6 months old who looked less at people's eyes in videos were more likely to be given an autism diagnosis at age 3 and that eye-tracking could provide an early indicator of autism.

Experts said that because the study shows that a social behavior that is significantly different in children with autism is strongly influenced by genetics, it might help scientists home in on specific genes to better understand autism or at least a key autism characteristic.

Even when identical twins watched different videos, their results matched. "How much Twin 1 looked at the eyes in a video that Twin 2 didn't get to see predicted how much Twin 2 would look at the eyes in a different video," Dr. Jones said.

That suggests, he said, that the genetically driven behavior involves "seeking out" social information found in the eyes rather than "merely responding to" facial features, a finding that could help pinpoint "what is disrupted in children with autism as they develop and learn about the world."

Nelson cautioned against overemphasizing the direct role of genes. "Twins have identical DNA, but they don't have identical experiences and they don't have the same brains," he said. Most likely, through evolution, we came to have "genes that regulate the formation of the neural circuits that underpin how we visually inspect the social world," he said. "That helps ensure that we are social beings." ●

Baby Teeth Can Link Pregnancy And Autism

Those links, showing chemical exposure to the fetus, do not mean the mother did something to cause the condition.

BY PERRI KLASS, M.D.

If you are a parent worrying through pregnancy, or maybe trying to make sense of your child's neurodevelopmental problems, you aren't always glad to see another story about a new study looking at possible environmental risk factors. From pesticides in the food to phthalates in the plastics to pollutant particles in the air, so many different exposures have been linked to problems in the developing fetal brain that parents can sometimes feel at once bewildered and, inevitably, at fault for failing or having failed to take all possible precautions.

That's a great pity, because the accumulating research is of tremendous value, particularly to families struggling with an autism diagnosis. But there's an unfortunate tendency to treat each new study as a single explanatory solution to what is in fact a complicated and multifactorial issue.

Autism is "a very diverse condition — not all kids with autism are alike," said Dr. Leonardo Trasande, the director of the division of environmental pediatrics and a professor of pediatrics, environmental medicine and population health at New York University School of Medicine. "There are a lot of shades of gray and a lot of differential dysfunction," probably related to different parts of the brain, he said.

Dr. Craig Newschaffer, the founding director of the A.J. Drexel Autism Institute at Drexel University, said that while it's very important for the public to be aware that there are environmental risk factors in the development of autism, "pointing a finger at mom is not the endgame of this kind of research. The endgame isn't going to be about individual decision making, but more about informing policy."

"I very much agree this is not about blaming the parent in any way," said Dr. Manish Arora, professor of environmental medicine and public health at Icahn School of Medicine at Mount Sinai. "It's very hard to buy your way out of exposures; many exposures are present everywhere."

From a research point of view, Dr. Arora said, one challenge has been to measure toxic chemicals and exposures during fetal development, and connect them with an outcome like autism, which is diagnosed years later. He has developed an innovative technique using baby teeth, which start to develop toward the end of the first trimester, and form a new layer each day, growing in what he called an "incremental archival manner." The layers can capture traces of chemicals, so that they serve as "biologic hard drives," records of what exposures occurred during fetal development, and when they occurred, in a manner similar to the rings on trees.

Using the teeth that children have shed between the ages of 6 and 12, Dr. Arora said, it's possible to look back at exposures during fetal development, and at other aspects of early metabolism, to see whether children who later go on to develop autism are biologically different early on. In a study published in Science Advances in May 2018, scientists used

The original version of this article appeared on July 2, 2018. It has been edited for clarity and length.

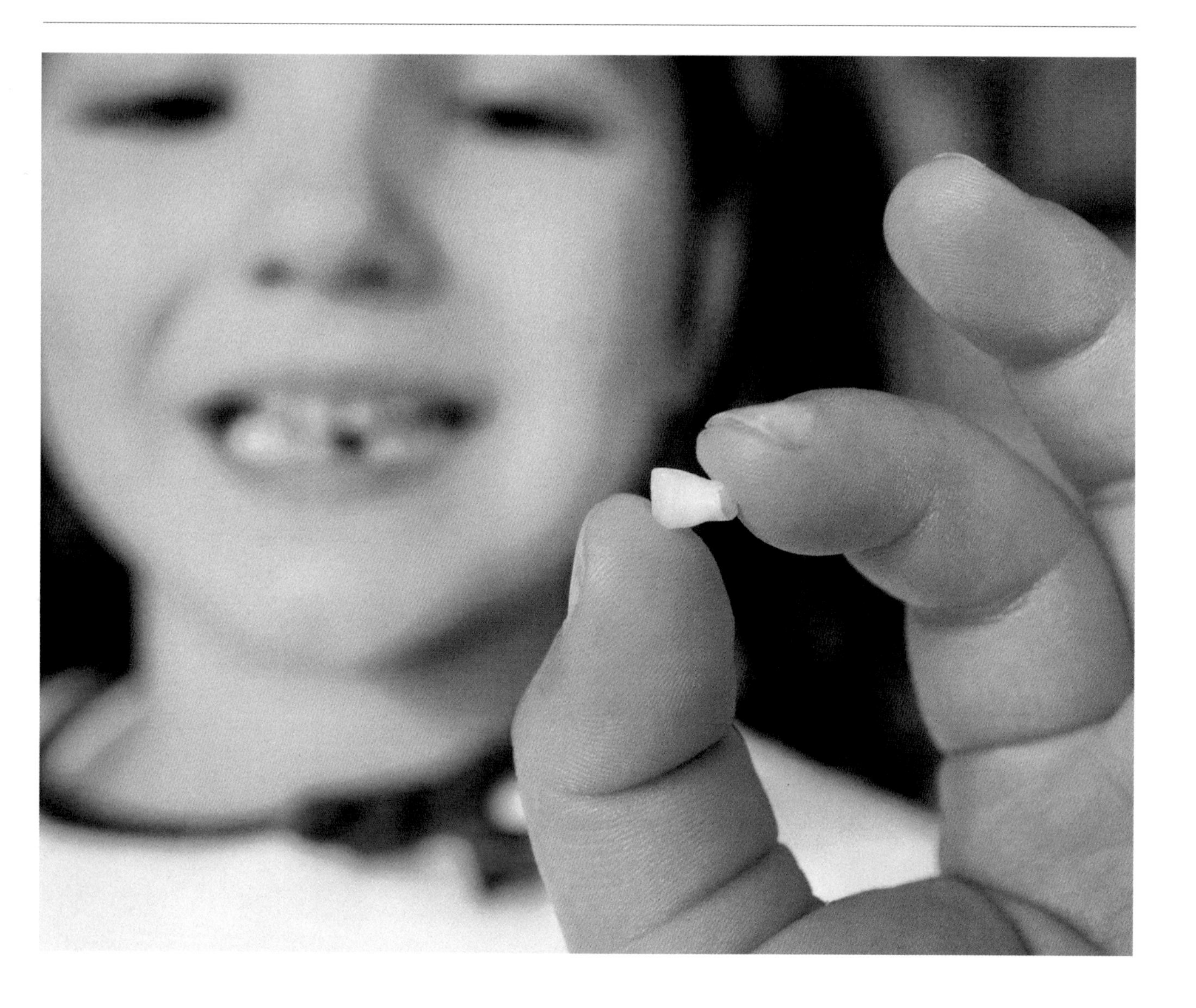

In baby teeth, which grow in an "incremental archival manner," layers capture chemical traces.

this technique to compare early zinc and copper metabolism in children with autism with their siblings without autism.

Dr. Paul Curtin, an assistant professor of environmental medicine and public health at Mount Sinai, who was first author on the study, said that in children with autism, regulation of zinc and copper metabolism shows differences beginning early in the course of fetal development. The point of the study was not to look at whether a child had been externally exposed to these metals, but rather at the internal metabolic rhythms of nutrients and possible toxins, at "what are the dynamics of zinc and copper metabolism, and how are those dysregulated in disease."

Dr. Arora said this could lead to a biomarker for autism, a diagnostic test that could be administered before a child shows behavioral differences. Could finding ways to correct that disrupted pathway alter a child's neurodevelopment?

"For the first time we have a biochemical pathway which, if we could modify, could have some effects," Dr. Arora said. "If it turns out to be causal, there might be a therapeutic benefit — I doubt if this is the only pathway in autism, but if it is one of the more important ones, we might have something."

Using baby teeth offers a remarkable new technique for looking back at all kinds of exposures during pregnancy. "Epidemiologists like myself are thrilled," Dr. Newschaffer said. However, he said, "it's very exciting but extremely early days."

And there is never going to be one simple answer. "There are so many factors that likely contribute to the origins of autism," Dr. Trasande said. "It's impossible to point to any one factor for any one child," he said. "We always speak about larger populations."

From an epidemiologic point of view, Dr. Newschaffer said, the effects of any one exposure are likely to be of small magnitude for any one individual. The important gains in reducing autism would be seen at the population level, and therefore, the best response to the research about environmental risks would be policy change to protect the whole population.

But until those policy changes are enacted, individuals may still want to reduce their exposures and to be particularly careful during pregnancy, avoiding pesticides, for example, by buying organic produce, if that is economically feasible. "You can be a little more cautious during this time," Dr. Newschaffer said.

"The other way more generally to limit the effect of these chemicals on the brain is healthy diet and particularly iodine," to protect the thyroid, Dr. Trasande said, since hypothyroidism, both in children and in mothers, is emerging as a possible contributing factor to autism. And after a child is born, "we can make sure families are eating healthier diets and having the best possible environment for raising their children."

Dr. Newschaffer said that autism researchers had previously been surprised by the link between exposure to air pollution and autism. Over 25 epidemiologic studies have found an association between prenatal and early postnatal air pollution exposure and autism.

Women who have higher air pollution exposures may be living in neighborhoods where there are other exposures, he said, but still, there is an emerging body of evidence to support the association.

"Air pollution" is a very heterogeneous term, and different studies have suggested a range of pollutants as more closely linked. Other associations between prenatal risk factors and autism development are also complicated, Dr. Newschaffer said. There appears to be a connection with advanced parental age, both of the mother and of the father, and an association between autism and very closely spaced pregnancies.

Autism risk is associated with a range of perinatal and neonatal complications, but as with air pollution, it's not a simple picture, because there are many different complications, and there is not one simple or consistent relationship. There could conceivably be some biological mechanism that might be activated by a range of different complications, Dr. Newschaffer said, but whatever the mechanism — and people have suggested inflammation or hormone pathways — "having a complicated pregnancy does increase your risk of a child having autism."

Still, he said, most pregnancies with complications do not result in a child with autism.

Dr. Trasande said he tells families that the strongest evidence we have of chemicals affecting the developing brain is about pesticides and flame retardants, which can be hard to avoid. People can reduce some exposures by eating organic produce, and opening windows to recirculate air and get rid of chemical dust, but it would take regulation to get some of these very persistent pollutants out of the home.

"The biggest impact here in autism and other environmentally driven conditions would be at the policy level," Dr. Arora said. "We are exposing our populations to many chemicals which are untested." ●

No, the Measles Vaccine Does Not Cause Autism

BY JAN HOFFMAN

At a time when measles outbreaks are mounting among clusters of unvaccinated children, notably in Washington State, New York and Texas, a new large study has found no association between the measles vaccine and autism — a reason often given by parents for rejecting inoculation.

The new research confirms what has long been widely accepted in the scientific community, and it echoes findings of a 2002 study by members of the same team of scientists about the vaccine, known as MMR because it protects against measles, mumps and rubella.

But the findings come at a moment of resurging suspicion about vaccine safety that has been promulgated at the far edges of the internet and on mainstream sites such as Amazon, Facebook and Pinterest. Many of those companies have taken recent steps to remove anti-vaccine content, and the president of the American Academy of Pediatrics, Dr. Kyle E. Yasuda, has written to the chief executives of Google, Facebook and Pinterest, urging further action in "an urgent request to work together to combat the dangerous spread of vaccine misinformation online."

In emphatic language, the researchers, who followed 657,461 Danish children born between 1999 and 2010, stated in the Annals of Internal Medicine: "The study strongly supports that MMR vaccination does not increase the risk for autism, does not trigger susceptible children, and is not associated with clustering of autism cases after vaccination."

Denmark offers a national vaccination program that is free and voluntary. At regular intervals, a team led by Dr. Anders Hviid, who is with the department of epidemiology research at Statens Serum Institut in Copenhagen, followed the children, 31,619 of whom remained unvaccinated.

The original version of this article appeared on March 5, 2019. It has been edited for clarity and length.

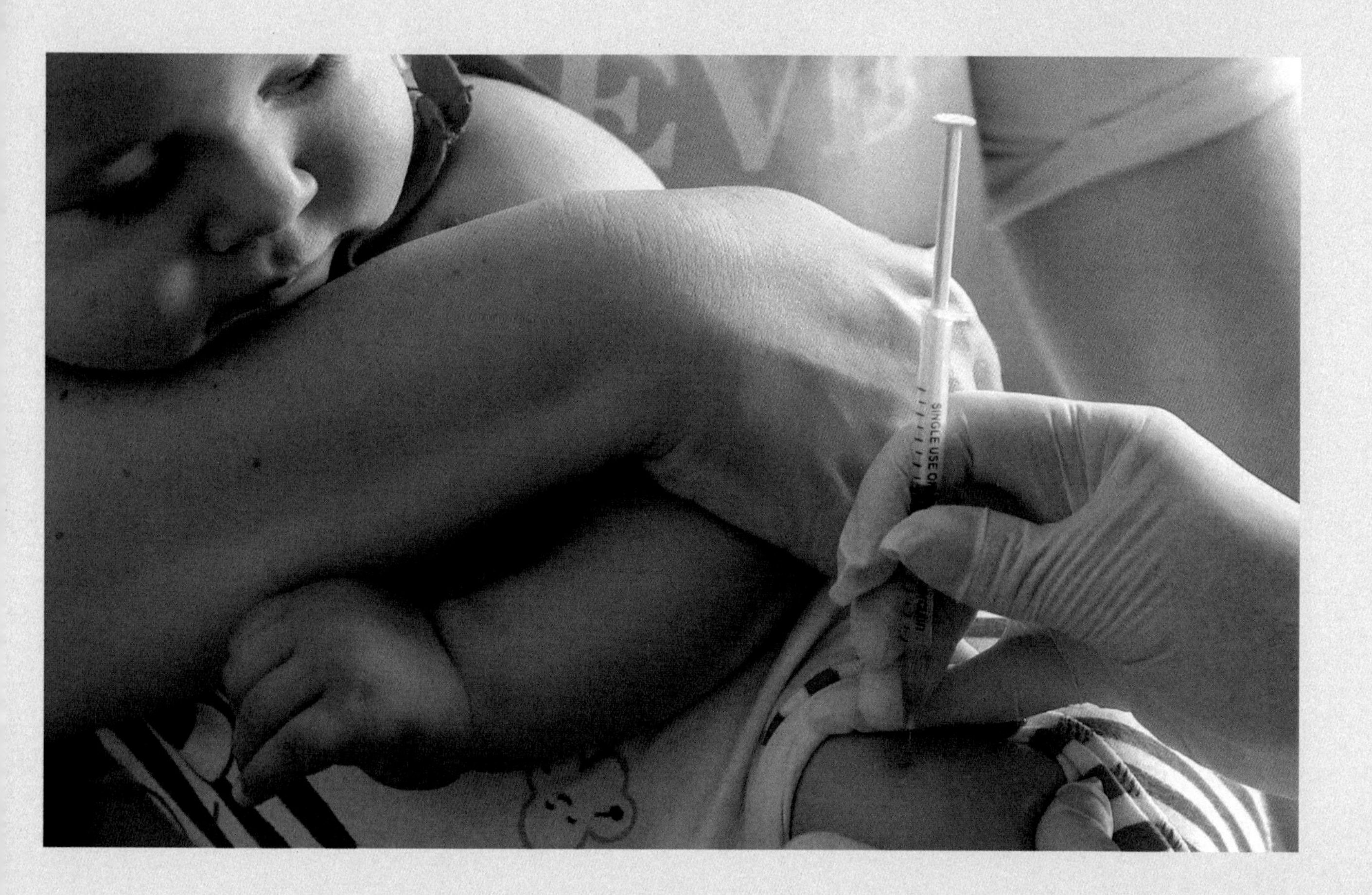

Doctors are emphatic about debunking the myth of a link between vaccines and autism.

The researchers identified subgroups of children according to other inoculations, and whether they had siblings with autism.

In time, 6,517 children received a diagnosis of autism. These researchers found no greater proportional incidence of the diagnosis between the vaccinated and unvaccinated children.

Noting that measles outbreaks are becoming more commonplace in the United States as well as Europe, Dr. Hviid said, "U.S. researchers concluded that even a 5 percent reduction in vaccination coverage would triple measles cases, with significant health economic costs. A main reason that parents avoid or are concerned about childhood vaccinations has been the perceived link to autism."

The results of his study, Dr. Hviid said, offered both reassurance and reliable data that no such link exists.

In an editorial accompanying the study, Dr. Saad B. Omer, who was a public health researcher at Emory University at the original time of publication, and Dr. Inci Yildirim at the Emory School of Medicine, pointed out that it has been nearly a decade since the small study which set off alarms about a possible link between the vaccine and autism has been refuted and retracted. Yet resources are being continually poured into studies such as this latest one, to underscore the inaccuracy of that original misfire.

"In an ideal world," they wrote, "vaccine safety research would be conducted only to evaluate scientifically grounded hypotheses, not in response to the conspiracy du jour."

They said that doctors and public health officials needed to firmly label the association "a myth."

"Debunking a myth is tricky," said Dr. Sean T. O'Leary, a spokesman for the American Academy of Pediatrics and an associate professor of pediatrics at the University of Colorado at Denver. When you repeat the myth, he said, "you risk reinforcing it. All that parents remember about your complicated explanation about why vaccines don't cause autism is that they're somehow linked. So pediatricians should focus on the diseases we're trying to prevent and if you have to address a myth, be clear that's exactly what it is."

Aiding The Autistic

It is important to understand that autism manifests itself in sharply different ways depending upon where someone sits on the so-called spectrum. Those with "severe autism" have far different needs than those on the spectrum's opposite end. But it has become abundantly clear that many people with autism can lead satisfying and productive lives when provided with the opportunity. Those opportunities are growing fast: integrated classrooms provide managed environments for autistic children; jobs and workplaces are designed to allow highly focused skills to flourish; more public spaces recognize the particular needs of the autistic — an absence of noise or bright lights, a refuge from crowds — and cater to those needs. Progress is evident.

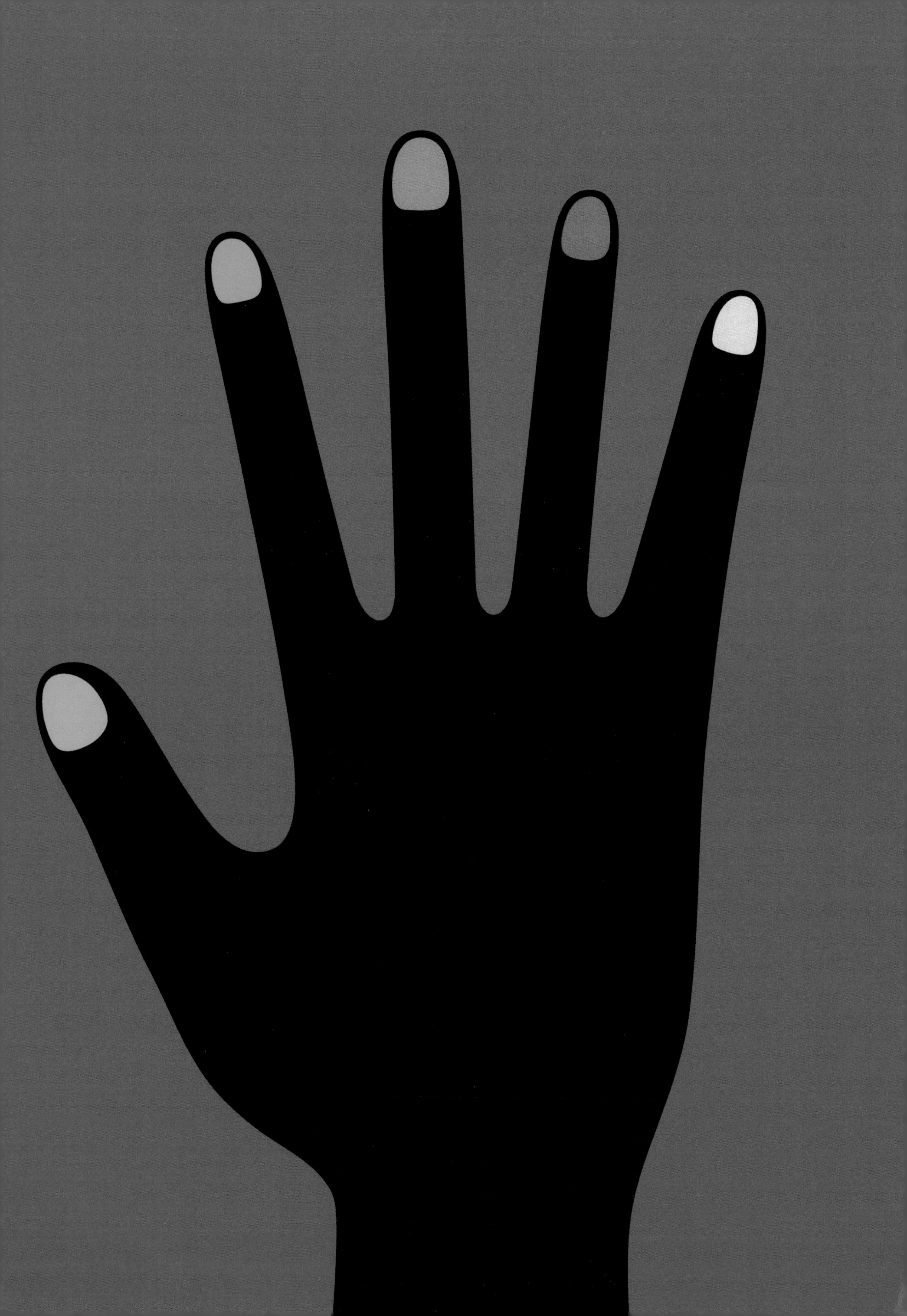

An Office With Room For Understanding

Some work spaces have a few employees with autism. This one is designed for them alone.

BY SUSAN DOMINUS

Before Ben Hirasuna showed up for the first job interview of his life, he went for weeks at a time without leaving his parents' home in Santa Monica. To say Hirasuna is shy is to say the ocean is big — it captures nothing of the vastness of the feeling. He managed to attend college at Arizona State for just over a year but returned home for good in November 2017. For a few months, he took some classes at a local community college, but eventually his routine gave way to solitude at home. During the day, he slept; at night he rose to battle the enemy in futuristic cities and pastel landscapes on his PC, or tinkered on another monitor with any of the codes he taught himself in high school. Finally, in November 2018, his parents insisted that he get a job — any job, at the bakery down the street or at McDonald's, if it came to that.

Hirasuna could not imagine a worse hell than a job in customer service, which would require, he sensed, a more cheerful public face than he could possibly muster. He remembered that in September, he went to an innovation fair at his old high school and met the head of a technology consulting business called Auticon, which specializes in hiring people who are, like Hirasuna, on the autism spectrum. He made an appointment with a recruiter at the office, and in January 2019, he forced himself to make the 10-minute drive to Auticon's office.

The original version of this article appeared on Feb. 21, 2019. It has been edited for clarity and length.

Offices, for plenty of people, can occasionally be overwhelming, crowded with feelings too big for cubicles, too personal for a professional setting. A higher-up checks a watch midconversation; a comment in a meeting is talked over; someone and someone else go to lunch. Doubts flourish under fluorescent lights that expose every slight, every interpersonal hurdle.

For Ben Hirasuna, the Auticon office calmed his fears of the stress of a social workplace and made his life a more productive one.

And then there are people like Hirasuna; people who feel bombarded by those same clues and cues, all the while knowing they are unreliable interpreters of their meaning. For some people with autism, socializing is an elaborate game with more exceptions than rules, so that any small decision — hover outside the boss's office? don't hover? — poses an insurmountable challenge.

Guesswork is prevalent, misapprehension the norm. "When it is hard to read the room, so to speak, it does morph into anxiety over time," said Grey Patton, a 23-year-old employee on the spectrum who graduated from the University of California, Riverside, and who, like Hirasuna, started working at Auticon in 2019. "It's moving in the dark without a flashlight."

One Auticon employee compared his experience at his last job to the television show "Survivor." The interview process alone is a sociability test that many people with autism are destined to fail or inclined to avoid altogether.

Major technology businesses like Microsoft and SAP have made significant efforts over the past several years to hire more people with strong cognitive skills who are on the spectrum, recognizing that they represent untapped potential in the job market. Auticon goes one step further; it is an office where people who have autism are a majority. Employees on the spectrum do not make up a pod within a company; instead, they define the predominant culture.

Many businesses that recruit people with autism specialize, like Auticon, in quality assurance, which is like a poultry-inspection service for software. Is the log-in working on the home page? What happens if someone right-clicks on this other link? The work can be rote and entry-level or require more skilled analysts to write scripts that test that software automatically, "essentially to see if I can break it," as Hirasuna put it.

In 2013, around the same time technology companies first started expanding their hiring of people with autism, Gray Benoist, a father of two sons on the spectrum, plotted out a business for the express purpose of securing his children's future. He knew they were smart and capable; he also knew, as he put it, "that they present themselves in ways that may not be corporate-America kinds of ways." He moved his family from St. Louis, where he had been the chief financial officer of an industrial-product business, and started over in Santa Monica, to create a software quality-assurance business that expanded its offerings over time. With a few partners, he founded MindSpark as a California benefit corporation, a type of for-profit business. It is founded on the radical proposition that social purpose and employee well-being are as essential to their mission as profit.

A new chair in the entry area has proved popular — some staff members avoid the small couch opposite the chair, for fear someone will sit too close to them.

Within five years, the business was thriving, with two offices, one in Culver City and the other in Santa Monica. The company had about 32 employees, ranging from entry-level trainees to skilled automation analysts, all of whom were on the spectrum, as well as about seven neurotypical managers and administrators. In 2018, Auticon, a German company based in Munich, a business also devoted to employing people on the spectrum, acquired Benoist's start-up.

A business full of people who are on the autism spectrum provides its own kinds of managerial and interpersonal challenges, but to be the norm in an office, rather than an exception, is an unqualified relief for many of Auticon's employees. Hirasuna noticed the difference in the first week of work, when he was writing an email to his manager. "I realized, after the first day, 'Oh yeah, I don't have to read this over for nuance and all that stuff,'" he said. In college, he hated emailing his professors, because he agonized over whether his tone was too forceful or too presumptuous or too inarticulate. At Auticon, he said, he felt a release in simply writing an email, reading it over for typos and sending it out. What was the worst his boss was going to think if he sent out a tone-deaf email? "'That's autism!'" Hirasuna said with a big, comedic shrug. "'O.K. — that's what we expected!'"

A culture of acceptance occasionally conflicts with a training environment intended to prepare the staff for the possibility of working in a more typical office. Rebecca Beam, a longtime tech recruiter who became president of Auticon when the company acquired MindSpark, sensed early on that many Auticon employees felt uneasy when she stopped by their desks in the morning with a big hello. Many of them were uncomfortable with small talk; they had no interest in rehashing their weekends or looking at pictures of Ziggy, Beam's terrier mix; but Beam saw a morning greeting as the bare minimum of office socializing, a nicety they might as well endure, if only for practice.

Before working for the company, Beam had no personal connection to someone with autism but believes all individuals deserve work worthy of their talents. And before she was put in charge of Auticon's United States business in June 2018, she hadn't known the staff well enough to realize, as she eventually did, that every decision, no matter how small, mattered.

In her first weeks on the job, Beam made what turned out to be a bold move: She gave the Santa Monica office a small makeover, trying to brighten it with some new furniture for the front entryway, a smattering of succulents, some framed posters of illustrated animals. Over a weekend, she also had a wall, once white, painted gray.

That Monday, Max Gadson, a 24-year-old analyst who has been with the company for two years, arrived at the office and stopped short, taking in all this newness. He knew something was happening — they had been told to clear their desks — but no one knew exactly what. No one said anything about the wall being painted, much less that it would be gray, and here it was Monday, and now, boom! Gray wall. Gadson does not have obsessive-compulsive disorder, but he imagined that this feeling was a bit like that, the sense that something was out of order. He did not understand why the wall color had changed and sought out his supervisor to talk it through.

Another co-worker, Gray Benoist Jr. (the son of MindSpark's founder), who is 31, took issue with a new patterned chair now placed in the entry area.

The chair would later prove popular — some staff mem-

bers avoid the small couch opposite the chair, for fear someone will sit too close to them — but certainly, in the beginning, Beam could tell some employees were out of sorts. One analyst asked why she insisted on placing succulents in the Culver City office when, as he sees it, they were so clearly superfluous. On another occasion, she moved a young man's desk without consulting him, and he temporarily quit. For most of Beam's staff, she realized over time, there is no such thing as a pleasant surprise (unless it's pizza).

"People with my type of disorder, it's not that we don't have emotion," Gadson said. "It's that we have too much emotion. We can't push that stuff back."

Beam, as she started to understand the office's workings, gave a lot of thought, in her first month, to the size of a couch she was buying for a conference room in Culver City, until the question was no longer about a couch and more about a culture. She knew that if she bought one that was long, employees would sleep on it and not just doze, sitting, with their eyes closed, but stretch out and slumber deeply. Many of her employees have poor sleep habits; some are on medication that can affect their sleep. Would Auticon, going forward, be a place where you could regularly lie down and nap during lunch in the conference room, so long as you made it back to your desk on time? Or was it going to be a place where that was considered inappropriate?

Employees at Auticon often prefer to work with the lights dimmed, or even off.

In the end, Beam decided to lean into the notion of the workplace as an accommodating space: She bought the big couch. At lunch, someone is usually napping on it, even when other employees are playing Ping-Pong on the conference table, their jackets strewn across it for a net.

Accommodations that would seem unusual at another office seem perfectly reasonable to the employees at Auticon. At the Culver City office, overhead lights bothered one or two colleagues so much that everyone agreed to work without artificial lights, so that often, by the end of the day, they are all working in pitch darkness, rectangles of soft, bright light from their computers illuminating their faces.

Absences, in general, are not encouraged, but they are accepted as a cost of doing business with a population that often experiences depression. Managers adjust, within reason, to their employees' boundaries, rather than the other way around, such as when employees suffering from gastrointestinal problems — a little-understood but common issue for some people on the spectrum — call in to explain, in great detail, why they won't be coming in that day.

Another employee had disappeared, without notice, for several days, and his managers were afraid for his safety. "You know, some employers would say to someone like that, 'I'm done,'" Beam said. "But I'm going to work with that person and work with that person, because I see the potential."

Some Auticon employees have skills that would likely earn them higher pay were they employed at a big company in the United States. But Auticon invests heavily in their training and offers the kind of bespoke workplace systems that allow for their success, even for analysts in entry-level jobs. It employs analysts with advanced degrees from top universities and people who failed to make it through college, people whose minds work at high operating speed and some with short-term memory challenges (and some with both). Somehow the balance of talents and abilities keeps the operation afloat.

"I kind of like it here," Hirasuna said, a month into his job. He was learning new programming skills he wouldn't have acquired on his own. He felt the strain of leaving the house every day but also, he had to admit, some relief. As workplaces go, this one was relatively painless: "They accept me as I am." ●

How Technology Is Closing The Job Gap

Adults on the autism spectrum often have difficulty finding employment. Entrepreneurs and advocates are working to fix that by pairing companies with a pool of candidates.

BY ELLEN ROSEN

Leon Campbell, the first autistic employee at Daivergent, now holds a key quality-control position at the tech company.

Byran Dai was 24 when he promised his mother, who passed away less than two months later, that he would look out for his younger brother Brandon, who is autistic. Brandon, 15 at the time, was receiving special education and social services, but Byran knew that by 22, his brother would phase out of the services and education provided by the state. "In the autism community, we call that 'falling off the cliff,'" Byran said. "It's what a lot of families worry about."

About 50 percent of those on the autism spectrum have held at least one job since high school, but often that job is a low-paying, part-time position.

Like so many entrepreneurs inspired by personal experience, Dai's concern for his brother ultimately became the genesis for a new business. In 2018, Dai co-founded Daivergent, a start-up that is connecting tech companies with a pool of candidates on the autism spectrum. The company already has 20 corporate clients and has helped 75 people find work. There are about 1,100 candidates in the Daivergent pool.

The employment rate for individuals on the spectrum — even for those who have finished college — is extremely low. Statistics vary, but according to Anne Roux, a research scientist at the A.J. Drexel Autism Institute at Drexel University in Philadelphia, about 50 percent of those on the autism spectrum have had at least one job since high school, but often that job is a low-paying part-time position. For those with greater impairment, she added, only 14 percent have employment in the community in which they live.

It's not that their abilities are lacking, said David Kearon, the director of adult services for the advocacy group Autism Speaks. "Anecdotally what we hear all the time is that autistic adults have the intellectual capability, but, because of their challenges with social skills, they're often unemployed." Brandon Dai, for example, "can focus on detail-oriented, complex, repetitive kinds of work that underlie much of the data structure that go into artificial intelligence and machine learning," his brother said.

Dai, a data scientist, and a high school friend, Rahul Mahida, a data engineer who has an autistic cousin, realized that there was no platform to pair those on the spectrum with companies looking for candidates who could work in data and artificial intelligence.

Leon Campbell, 24, who is autistic, was employee No. 1 at the new company. With a computer science degree from Hunter College in New York, Campbell had technical skills but had never had a job before Daivergent hired him. He initially worked on labeling, but now focuses on quality assurance, overseeing the projects Daivergent's remote workers complete. "I am one of the last lines of defense," he said, before the work is sent to the corporate client.

He worried that his new job would be stressful, but because Dai and Mahida were so accommodating, "those concerns quickly faded away on the first week of the job."

Teaching the requisite skills is accomplished through video-based education. Mahida said the candidates often excel at the ability to vet thousands of images. "They do much better on these assessments than Byran and I did," he said.

The most difficult part may be improving social and communication skills. Daivergent, Dai said, builds "shared interest groups through community forum and instant messaging tools, and also creates virtual job clubs where folks on the spectrum can swap tips and review résumés. It creates a community by us, and for us."

Daivergent is not the only company helping autistic workers find employment. Brenda Weitzberg was one of the first entrepreneurs to tackle this issue. Nearly a decade ago, motivated by her oldest son, Weitzberg and her husband, Moshe, began their fledgling company. They parlayed their first client into others, and now the company, Aspiritech, has about 130 employees, neurodiverse as well as neurotypical.

While Aspiritech does not have specific training, the company has hired support staff to work with its employees. And the employees have formed clubs for after-work activities, increasing their social interactions. While autism inspired the company, Weitzberg said her company's focus was on the work. "Autism gets us a foot in the door, since many people have a child or family member with autism, but it doesn't keep us there. There has to be quality."

Dai and Mahida know this as well and, as a result, are deliberate in scaling their efforts. That is difficult because there is demand from the tech community, eager for capable employees. Dai hopes his brother will eventually be suitable for the platform: "He's well versed in his iPad and grew up with computers so I always thought of his potentially working somewhere in tech, likely more in a support role."

Growing the company has been a learning process for Dai and Mahida. "We don't say tech will solve everything. We have to understand the nuance first," Dai said. "We won't be the people who will say we know just what to do."

For companies — whether in tech or other industries — who want to add staff from the neurodiverse community, Leon Campbell, Daivergent's employee No. 1, has some advice: "I want an employer to see me as a person. Don't hire me because you want to look better for your investors." ●

The original version of this article appeared on Oct. 24, 2019. It has been edited for clarity and length.

Schools Replace 'Hush' With Help

Autistic children in New York City public schools benefit from a successful program of integrated classrooms, specially trained teachers and smaller class sizes.

BY KATE TAYLOR

For autistic children, Dorothy Siegel does not believe in paraprofessionals, the teaching assistants sometimes assigned to shadow students in class.

To show you why, Siegel, 70, a longtime special education advocate, grabs your arm, pokes you and forcibly turns your head toward the teacher, the way an aide might.

"The para is not someone who's there to help a child understand how to interpret the environment so he doesn't get upset," she said recently. "The para is there to keep him out of trouble, so they'll allow him to continue in that classroom."

Over the last 14 years, Siegel has tried to create a better way to teach students with autism. The program she started, called ASD Nest, is now in 39 elementary, middle and high schools in New York City. The aim is to help autistic students understand the school environment and their own needs, so they can function both in and out of school.

In 2017, 17,015 students in New York City public schools were classified as having autism as a disability, up from

---

The original version of this article appeared on June 14, 2017. It has been edited for clarity and length.

Teachers like Emily Lawrence, in an ASD Nest program class at Public School 682 in Brooklyn, help autistic students understand the school environment and their own needs.

For students both autistic and not, teachers in the Nest program do extensive modeling of appropriate social interaction.

13,685 in 2014-15. In recent years, a growing number of autistic students have been integrated into classrooms with general education students, with many of them being served in the Nest program.

"We basically cash in paraprofessionals and buy teachers," said Siegel, who has a round face, a halo of gray hair and a direct manner. "The whole goal of the Nest program is to replace people who hush children with teachers who understand children."

A Nest class typically has two certified teachers, four students with autism and eight to 20 general education students, depending on the grade. To get into the program, children with autism must be deemed capable of doing grade-level work. Three times a week they are pulled out for social development intervention, which is led by a speech therapist and is meant to teach students how to navigate social interactions.

Some parents ask for their general education children to be placed in a Nest class because of the smaller class size and the extra teacher, or because the program emphasizes teaching children to be kind and respectful to one another. Siegel explained that principals consider such requests but may have other priorities in putting the class together.

For Siegel, a former senior researcher for the New York University Institute for Education and Social Policy, Nest's mission is personal. Her son Sam, 34, is autistic. He attended two publicly funded private special education schools and graduated from New York University. But educational outcomes for most autistic children are grim. Only 36 percent of students in their 20s with autism attend any type of postsecondary school, according to the A.J. Drexel Autism Institute at Drexel University in Philadelphia. Siegel said her inspiration to start the program, which came while reading "Thinking in Pictures," Temple Grandin's memoir about autism, was "as much a call as any religious person has ever had."

To devise it, she teamed up with Shirley Cohen, a professor of special education at Hunter College in New York. (Nest teachers are required to take two graduate-level courses at Hunter focused on teaching children with autism.) They started the program in Public School 32, in Brooklyn's District 15, where Siegel had been on the school board and which former New York City Schools chancellor Carmen Fariña was then overseeing as a superintendent. Siegel said, "She called me in and she says, 'I want you to put this in every district.'"

At Public School 682, the Academy of Talented Scholars, in Bensonhurst, Brooklyn, on a spring morning, the techniques Nest uses were on display throughout the building. There was relatively little on classroom walls, because the usual jumble of posters and charts can be overwhelming to autistic students. In several classes, the lights were off, leaving the room in a kind of twilight.

Christina Ramsay, a fifth-grade teacher, said some autistic students find the lights visually overstimulating, while others have such sensitive hearing that they can hear the lights buzz. Her co-teacher, Neil Rathan, led the students in a math game in a voice so low and gentle that a visitor could barely hear him.

Some students had pedals, like those on bicycles, under their desks, to allow those who need to fidget to move their feet while they worked. Every Nest classroom had a corner outfitted with pillows or a rug, to which students could retreat to soothe themselves. To help students put small irritants and sources of distress in context, some classes had signs on the wall saying, "What kind of problem is this?!" and listing a 1-to-5 scale, with 1 being a "Little Problem" and 5 being an "Emergency Problem."

In Nest, teachers do a lot of modeling of appropriate social interaction. In a third-grade class, Michelle Dragisics divided the students into small groups to measure polygons in tape on the floor. In each group, one person was to take the measurements, one was supposed to help and another was to record.

A few minutes later, Dragisics noticed a boy in a black shirt sitting on the side of the room looking lost, so she led him to his group.

"Now that our whole group is here," she said, "let's make sure that everybody has a role."

Later, she explained, "We try to put a lot of the hidden curriculum of school on their radar." A teacher might say, for instance, "I wonder what so-and-so is thinking," or, "Your face is telling me that you're upset."

In social development intervention — or "social club," as the students called it — four fourth graders watched a video of strangers making conversation and finding things in common based on various prompts.

Deirdre Whiffin, a speech therapist, led a game in which each student wrote on a Post-it something they did over spring break, and then everyone had to guess who did what.

Some students at Public School 682 had pedals, like those on bicycles, under their desks, to allow those who need to fidget to move their feet while they worked.

"You have to go into your friend files," she said, gently suggesting to the children that it was important to try to retain information about other people, something that a child with autism might not understand.

The city has not methodically tracked outcomes for students in the program. Siegel said she knew anecdotally that at least half of the students in the two original classes in 2003 were in college, but she could not provide more detailed information.

Catherine Lord, the director of the Center for Autism and the Developing Brain, at NewYork-Presbyterian/Weill Cornell Medical Center, said she did not know of another program for autistic students that was as comprehensive and well organized, though she has not done a formal evaluation.

"I've been completely impressed," she said.

The Education Department is expanding the program, adding four more schools in 2018. And New York University, which houses the ASD Nest Support Project, which has six staff members, including Siegel, is working to expand the model outside New York. The city of Aarhus, Denmark, started its first Nest classes in 2016, and the Skaneateles Central School District in central New York is starting a Nest program as well, Siegel said.

Christina, a mother whose son is in second grade in a Nest class at Public School 84, the José De Diego School, in Brooklyn, and who did not want her last name used to protect her son's privacy, said that when her son was in prekindergarten, "he would come out with his fingers chewed to the bone from anxiety." But since he started in Nest in kindergarten, things have significantly improved, she said. He keeps a "body sock" — essentially a long, stretchy pillowcase — in a corner of the classroom that he can go into to calm himself if he gets anxious.

His classmates take that in stride. At that age, Siegel said, the children don't really notice that some of their classmates behave differently. "To a 5-, 6- or 7- year-old, everything is normal," she said. Though at 7 or 8 a child might say, "'Ooh, that's weird,'" she said. "Younger than that, kids just love each other." She added, "So you can build on that, and create great relationships." ●

Rolling Out The Welcome Mat For Uneasy Travelers

Families with an autistic child know how difficult travel can be. A growing number of theme parks and attractions are working to make things easier.

BY ELAINE GLUSAC

The Thibault family at Rio Secreto, Playa Del Carmen, Mexico, in 2017. From left, Chris, Sebastian, Tristan, Emerson and Nicole Thibault.

When Nicole Thibault had her first child, she imagined traveling everywhere with him. But by age 2, he would become upset simply passing a restaurant that smelled of garlic. Waiting in line elicited tantrums and crowded places overwhelmed him. Autism was diagnosed within the year.

"I thought maybe our family dream of travel wouldn't happen," said Thibault, 46, of Fairport, N.Y., who now has three children. But she spent the next three years learning to prepare her son for travel by having him watch videos of future destinations and attractions so that he would know what to expect. The preparation helped enable him, now 14 and well-traveled, to enjoy adventures as challenging as exploring caves in Mexico. It also encouraged Thibault to launch a business, Magical Storybook Travels, planning travel for families with special needs.

Now the travel industry is catching up to the family. A growing number of theme parks, special attractions and hotels are introducing autism training and sensory guides that highlight triggers, providing resources in times of need and assuring families they won't be judged.

Battling stigma, finding acceptance

Some children with autism spectrum disorder may have sensory sensitivities, and many have trouble adapting to changes in routine, which is the essence of travel. The growing frequency of autism diagnoses and the gap in travel services for those dealing with autism created an overlooked market.

"There's still a lot of stigma for families with children on the spectrum," said Meredith Tekin, the president of the International Board of Credentialing and Continuing Education Standards, which certifies organizations from schools to hospitals in cognitive disorders. In the past two to three years, the organization has worked with more than 100 travel providers on autism programs. "We went from zero in travel to getting requests from dozens and dozens of places," she said.

Some families skip travel altogether — an I.B.C.C.E.S. study found 87 percent of families whose children have autism don't take family vacations — but others insist it feeds minds and teaches coping skills.

"We're bringing up kids in a world that's constantly changing and the more we can do to make them a little bit more comfortable with change, the better," said Alan Day, a travel agent who founded Autism Double-Checked, a consultancy that trains travel companies in autism readiness, after he was told his own son was on the spectrum.

Autism isn't just a childhood issue, of course. Stephen Gaiber, 30, of Irvine, Calif., began writing the Autistic Traveler blog last year to share his experiences and embolden others like him to travel. "I fear being misunderstood or not knowing what to do," he said. "I strive to be mainstream and know what I'm supposed to do by planning ahead."

Autism-friendly theme parks

I.B.C.C.E.S. certification requires 80 percent of staff members who interact with guests to undergo up to 21 hours of training in sensory awareness, communication and social skills; to pass an exam demonstrating their understanding; and to be recertified every two years. Among the recently certified destinations are SeaWorld Orlando, the Aquatica Orlando and Discovery Cove, where visitors can swim with dolphins and snorkel with tropical fish. All three were certified last spring.

Additionally, the International Board created sensory guides for the parks, available online, that rate attractions on a scale of one to 10 in five senses — touch, taste, sound, smell and sight. There are also corresponding signs in parks with sensory ratings.

"We're not asking SeaWorld not to be SeaWorld, but to provide families with options," Tekin said, stressing the importance of having materials available before a visit, which allows families to discuss what to expect and anticipate any pitfalls. Each park also created a quiet room with neutral décor, minimal noise, lighting on dimmer switches and interactive toys where families can take a time out.

Resorts, malls and destinations

The website Autism Travel (autismtravel.com) lists I.B.C.C.E.S.-certified destinations including Beaches Resorts, the three family-friendly all-inclusives in Jamaica and the Turks & Caicos, that qualified in 2017. In April, the resorts received advanced certification, introducing new one-on-one childcare, a private room for check-in and a culinary program that allows for a greater range of special requests.

The most ambitious among autism-spectrum efforts is in Mesa, Ariz., which draws significant family traffic with Major League Baseball spring training. The city aims to be the first autism-certified travel destination in the country, requiring 60 members of its travel bureau, Visit Mesa, including hotels and attractions, to undergo autism training and implement programs.

For Marc Garcia, the chief executive of Visit Mesa, the program was born of personal experience; he has a 5-year-old with autism among three children. "We travel like other people and we've received the strange looks and awkward stares when your child acts up and has a tantrum at a hotel, restaurant or attraction and it's uncomfortable," he said.

Inclusion, he added, is both good practice and good business. "If you're friendly to a community, that word spreads fast and they become hyper-loyal. We thought it was a good opportunity to do business and to get out in front of it." ●

The original version of this article appeared on July 11, 2019. It has been edited for clarity and length.

Does Google Glass Have an Afterlife Teaching Children?

It failed with the general public, but researchers believe that the computerized eyewear and other technologies could help autistic children recognize emotion.

BY CADE METZ

When Esaïe Prickett sat down in the living room with his mother, father and four older brothers, he was the only one wearing Google Glass.

As Esaïe, who was 10 at the time and is 13 now, gazed through the computerized glasses, his family made faces — happy, sad, surprised, angry, bored — and he tried to identify each emotion. In an instant, the glasses told him whether he was right or wrong, flashing tiny digital icons that only he could see.

Esaïe was 6 when he and his family learned he had autism. The technology he was using while sitting in the living room was meant to help him learn how to recognize emotions and make eye contact with those around him. The glasses would verify his choices only if he looked directly at a face.

He and his family tested the technology for several weeks as part of a clinical trial run by researchers at Stanford University in and around the San Francisco Bay Area. As detailed in The Journal of the American Medical Association, Pediatrics, the trial fits into a growing effort to build new technologies for children on the autism spectrum, including interactive robots and computerized eyewear.

The Stanford study's results show that the methods have promise and indicate that they could help children like Esaïe understand emotions and engage in more direct ways with those around them. They could also measure changes in behavior, something that has historically been difficult to do.

Esaïe Prickett wearing Google Glass at his home in Morgan Hill, Calif., where he and his family tested the device in a clinical trial.

Experts believe that other new technologies may help in similar ways. Talking digital assistants like Amazon's Alexa, for example, could help children who misuse their pronouns. However, even as these ideas spread, researchers warn that they will require rigorous testing before their effects are completely understood.

Catalin Voss started building software for Google Glass in 2013, not long after Google unveiled the computerized eyewear amid much hullabaloo from the national media. An 18-year-old Stanford freshman at the time, Voss began building an application that could automatically recognize images. Then he thought of his cousin, who had autism.

Growing up, Voss's cousin practiced recognizing facial expressions while looking into a bathroom mirror. Google Glass, Voss thought, might improve on this common exercise. Drawing on the latest advances in computer vision, his software could automatically read facial expressions and keep close track of when someone recognized an emotion and when they did not. "I was trying to build software that could recognize faces," Voss said. "And I knew that there were people who struggled with that."

At the time, Google stopped selling the device to consum-

The original version of this article appeared on July 17, 2019. It has been edited for clarity and length.

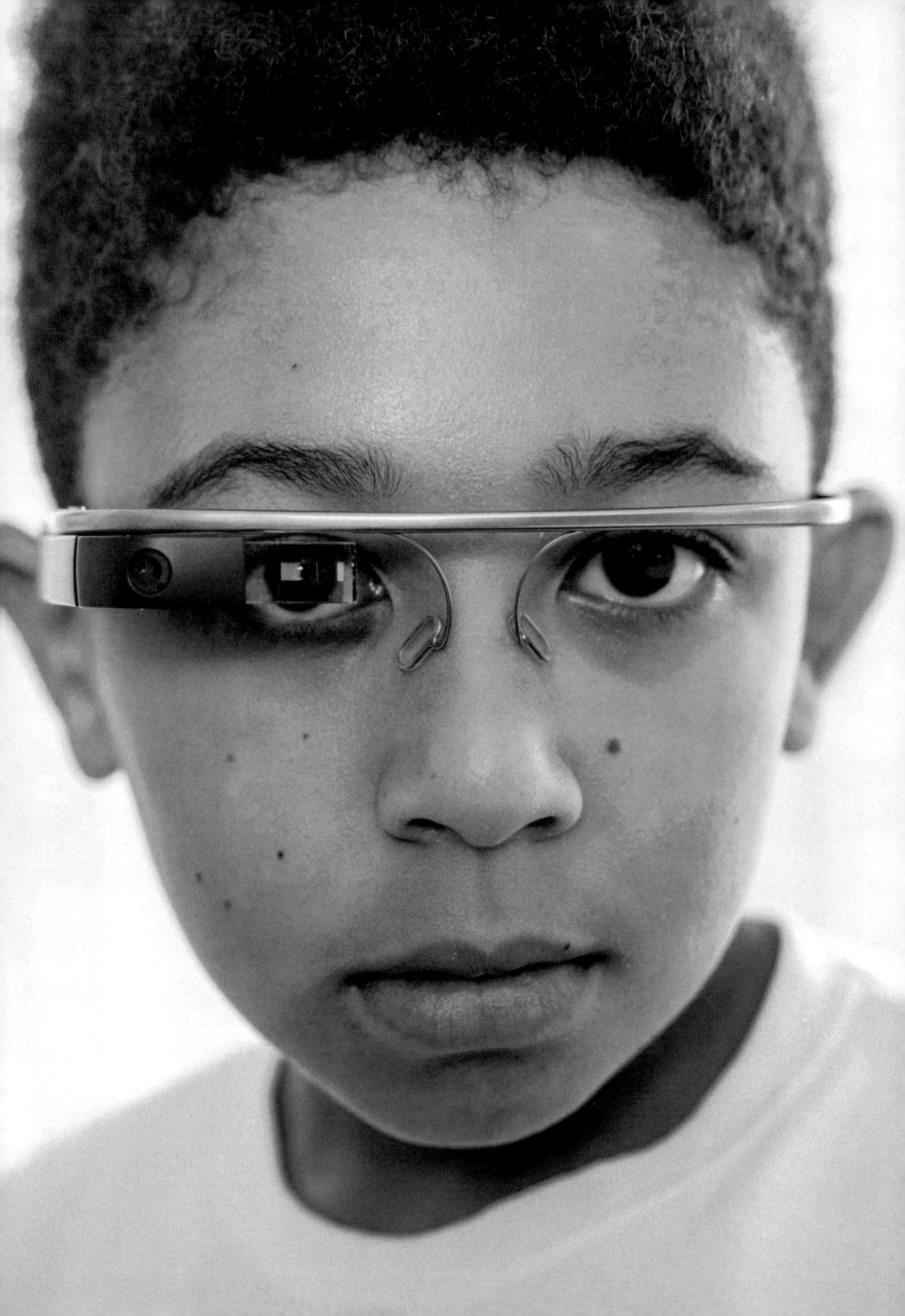

ers amid concerns that its built-in camera would compromise personal privacy. But Google Glass lived on as something to be used by researchers and businesses, and Voss, who had become a Ph.D. student, spent the next several years developing his application with Stanford professor Dennis Wall, who specializes in autism research.

Their clinical trial, conducted over two years with 71 children, is one of the first of its kind. It spanned everything from severe forms of autism, including children with speech impairments and tactile sensitivities, to much milder forms. Children who used the software in their homes showed a significant gain on the Vineland Adaptive Behavior Scales, a standard tool for tracking behavior on the autism spectrum.

The gain was in line with improvements by children who received therapy in dedicated clinics through more traditional methods. "It is a way for families to, on some level, provide their own therapy," Voss said.

Jeffrey Prickett, Esaïe's father, said he had been drawn to the study because he had known it would appeal to his son, who enjoys using iPad apps and watching DVD movies.

"He does fine interacting with people," Mr. Prickett said. "But he does better interacting with technology."

Prickett found it hard to judge whether the Google device helped his son recognize emotions, but he saw a marked improvement in Esaïe's ability to make eye contact.

Heather Crowhurst, who lives near Sacramento, said she had experienced something similar with her 8-year-old son, Thomas, who also participated in the trial. But Thomas was not entirely captivated with the digital therapy. "It was kind of boring," he said.

The concern with such studies is that they rely on the observations of parents who are helping their children use the technology, said Catherine Lord, a clinical psychologist at the University of California, Los Angeles. The parents are aware of the technological intervention, so their observations may not be reliable.

Still, the Stanford team considers its study a first step toward wider use of this and other technologies in autism. It has licensed the technology to Cognoa, a Silicon Valley start-up founded by Dr. Wall. The company hopes to commercialize the method, but that may still be years away. Brain Power, a start-up in Massachusetts that has built similar software for Google Glass, is selling its technology to local schools.

Patrick Daly, the assistant superintendent of the school district in North Reading, Mass., is testing Brain Power's technology after watching its effect on his 9-year-old son, who is on the spectrum. Previously, the district tried to teach similar skills through iPad computer tablets. Daly sees Google Glass as a big improvement.

"It can actually maintain eye contact," he said. "They are not looking down while they try to learn an emotion."

Robokind, a start-up in Dallas, applies the same philosophy to different hardware. The company spent the past several years designing a robot that attempts to teach many of the same skills as technologies built for digital eyewear. Called Milo, the doll-like, two-foot-tall robot mimics basic emotions and tries to make eye contact with students. It also asks questions and tries to engage students in simple conversations. Robokind has sold hundreds of the robots to schools for testing. Each one costs $12,000, plus more than $3,500 for additional software.

In some ways, such a device is a poor substitute for real human interaction. But the strength of this and other technologies is that they can repeat tasks time and again, without getting tired or bored or angry.

For these reasons, Pam Feliciano, the scientific director of the nonprofit Simons Foundation Powering Autism Research, also sees promise in Amazon's Alexa. Her 14-year-old son is on the spectrum and struggles with his pronouns. He sometimes calls himself "you," not "I."

Her task is to correct him each time he makes a mistake. But she's human and gets tired. She does not always remember. A device like Alexa could help, she said, provided that researchers can show it is reliable and effective.

"The technologies are there," she said. "It is just a matter of the right technologists working with the right clinicians." ●

Esaïe practicing facial expressions with his brother Morgan while wearing Google Glass.

Muffling the Crowd's Roar

BY JERÉ LONGMAN

Franco Buttaro, with his mom, Dana, played in the Eagles' new sensory room. Such spaces are proliferating in many of America's stadiums and arenas, a boon to sports-loving autistic children and their parents.

Franco Buttaro, 6, a kindergartner with autism, grew anxious while waiting in line to enter a Philadelphia Eagles game. Once inside Lincoln Financial Field, his parents took him to a refuge called a sensory room that muffled noise from the arriving crowd, pregame music and fireworks.

There, Franco relaxed as he played with Slinky toys and the team mascot, Swoop, who is trained not to make sudden, exaggerated movements in front of this audience. Franco touched a display of soothing lights and rising bubbles and practiced his spelling with Legos on a wall-mounted replica of the Eagles' field, assisted by a behavior analyst employed by the team.

Then Franco headed to his seat in the stadium, wearing a pair of noise-canceling headphones. To his parents' surprise and delight, after a second visit to the sensory room at halftime, Franco made it through the entire game as the Eagles defeated the New York Jets.

The Eagles are among dozens of professional sports teams, and a smaller number of college teams, over the past few years to provide quiet spaces and other assistance for spectators with sensory challenges, who can be most acutely affected by the overwhelming environments.

"Having a space where it's calm and quiet, it allows Franco to hit the reset button," said his father, Frank. "It opens up the opportunity for people that would most likely not be able to take their child to a game."

Levi Douglas, 6, visited the Eagles' sensory room during his first NFL game with his mother, Chanté, who said, "My anxiety level was at 1,000 and it dropped to, like, five."

More than 60 other pro teams have partnered with KultureCity, a nonprofit founded in 2013 to make those with autism feel accepted and included in public spaces.

Jeffrey Lurie, the Eagles' owner, whose younger brother has autism, said, "Do you want to embrace those who are a little different? Or do you want to shun them as we're seeing so often in our society today?"

The original version of this article appeared on Nov. 4, 2019. It has been edited for clarity and length.

OPINION

How to Meet Autistic People Halfway

It is a mistake to assume that those with autism do not want to be sociable. They are, instead, often just unable to respond in the ways we want and expect them to.

BY VIKRAM K. JASWAL AND NAMEERA AKHTAR

Children with autism, like everyone on the spectrum, have the basic human need for socializing with others. It's up to the rest of us to meet them on their terms.

One of the most widely held beliefs about autistic people — that they are not interested in other people — is almost certainly wrong. Our understanding of autism has changed quite a bit over the past century, but this particular belief has been remarkably persistent.

Seventy-five years ago, the first published account of autism described its subjects as "happiest when left alone" and "impervious to people." Even now, a National Institutes of Health fact sheet suggests that autistic people are "indifferent to social engagement," and the Centers for Disease Control and Prevention claims that some "might not be interested in other people at all."

There is no question that autistic people can seem as though they are not interested in others. They may not make eye contact or they may repeat lines from movies that don't seem relevant in the moment. They may flap their hands or rock their bodies in ways that other people find off-putting. But just because someone appears socially uninterested does not mean that he or she is.

As we point out in a paper published in June 2018 in Behavioral and Brain Sciences, many autistic people say they are very interested in, and in some cases desperate for, social connection. They experience loneliness and say they want friends. As the autistic author Naoki Higashida writes, "I can't believe that anyone born as a human being really wants to be left all on their own, not really," adding, "The truth is, we'd love to be with other people."

So why do autistic people act in ways that make it appear they want to be left alone? Autism is a neurological condition that affects how people perceive, think and move. Autistic people say that some of their apparently unsociable behaviors result from these neurological characteristics. Paradoxically, they may behave in these ways when they are trying to engage with other people.

Take eye contact. Some autistic people say they find sustained eye contact uncomfortable or even painful. Others report that it's hard to concentrate on what someone is saying while simultaneously looking at them. In other words, not looking someone in the eye may indicate that an autistic person is trying very hard to participate in the conversation at hand. Unfortunately, this attempt to engage often gets interpreted as a lack of interest. Or consider another common autistic behavior: echolalia. People who say the same thing over and over again can appear socially disengaged, but this does not mean that they are. Sometimes autistic people repeat phrases as a way of connecting at a deep level. For example, one autistic boy repeated, "Chicken Little thought the sky was falling, but the sky is not falling" when his mother was despondent over the death of a friend.

Paradoxically, not looking someone in the eye may indicate that an autistic person is trying very hard to participate in the conversation at hand.

Wrongly assuming that someone is not socially motivated can have devastating consequences. If you assume a person is not interested in interacting with you, then you probably won't exert much effort to interact in the first place. This can lead to a situation where neither person wants to interact with the other. Or you might insist that he or she interact in the ways you expect socially interested people to interact. Some popular autism interventions recommend that parents and teachers attempt to train autistic children to make eye contact or to stop repeating themselves. The problem with this is that the neurological makeup of an autistic person may make it difficult or impossible for him or her to do so.

Insisting that autistic people behave in ways that they are unable to can lead to feelings of learned helplessness, self-defeating thoughts and behaviors and, eventually, social withdrawal.

As an autistic participant in one study explained: "I have been endlessly criticized about how different I looked, criticized about all kinds of tiny differences in my behavior. There's a point where you say, 'To hell with it, it's impossible to please you people.'"

The danger of being assumed to be socially uninterested is especially acute for the roughly one-third of autistic people who do not use spoken language reliably. Like other autistic people, they behave in ways that get misinterpreted, and they may not be able to correct the record.

For all of us, whether we are socially motivated at any given time depends on much more than our innate predisposition for sociability. It also depends on how we've been treated in the past; our ability to tune out distracting sights, sounds, smells, thoughts and feelings; and the attitudes and behaviors of potential social partners.

Autistic people have been making the case for decades that they are interested in other people, and that they do not intend their unusual behaviors to indicate otherwise. So when someone does not make eye contact or repeats something you just said, be open to the possibility that it is just his or her way of trying to connect with you. Improving the social lives of autistic people will require putting aside assumptions about how social interest is expressed and recognizing that it can be shown in unexpected ways. ●

The original version of this article appeared on July 13, 2018. It has been edited for clarity and length. The authors are psychologists who study the social lives of autistic people.

GALLERY

Making New Connections

Therapies with communication can work. Here are four.

Body Language

Many therapies designed for the autistic have the primary aim of creating nonverbal communication. That makes sense, considering that a lack of verbal communication ability is a key and common aspect of autistic and other special-needs children. The belief is that the nonverbal is a steppingstone to verbal language. Dance is, in essence, nonverbal communication, and not surprisingly dance or movement therapy is among the most accepted and effective forms of treatment for many children with autism.

Practitioners speak often of "dances of relationship" and the "language of body movement" as avenues for connecting with children. Much of this occurs through "mirroring," a face-to-face copying of dance movements. Most dance therapy is one-on-one, but, as here at Ballet For All Kids in New York City, it can evolve into group sessions, which can improve body awareness and social skills — and add sheer joy.

Horse Play

Humans have long shared a special relationship with horses, and therapists have found that equine therapy (often called hippotherapy) can be highly effective with autistic children. It seems that the act of patting or brushing or hugging a horse can give a child a sense of simple physical communication, in lieu of more difficult human communication. Similarly, learning the clear body language of a horse helps in learning to recognize the often more complex clues of human body language.

At another level, learning to ride a horse aids in improving balance and spatial orientation. Here an autistic boy, Kai, 3, got comfortable at Ride On Therapeutic Horsemanship in California.

All on Board

One of the more surprisingly effective forms of autism therapy is, of all things, surfing. The idea sprouted some years ago in California (as pictured here, at a program called A Walk on Water, where instructors guide the board), but is now found on both U.S. coasts as well as in Australia and Britain. It is not fully understood why autistic children respond so positively to surfing (and, to be sure, some do not). But therapists suggest that water can have a calming effect on the autistic, enhanced by a pleasurable sense of weightlessness.

Parents have also found that a successful ride can instill a fresh sense of confidence in the child; surfing then becomes a family activity and an important source of bonding time.

A WALK ON WATER

Farm Friends

Interacting with animals other than horses has proven therapeutically valuable for the autistic — indeed, most domestic or farm animals seem to offer benefits. The basic theory as to why is much the same across species: People with autism struggle with human communication, in terms of both language and social skills, and, as one therapist put it, “animals are easier to understand than humans,” because their emotions are more consistent and their communication is nonverbal.

This understanding has led to a burgeoning number of farms that serve as boarding schools, camps and getaways for autistic children and children with special needs (such as, at left, Green Chimney Farm in Brewster, N.Y.). Besides the animals, there is a larger sense of life outdoors to experience, as one teacher put it, “the healing power of nature.”

Autism in Our Culture

Many of us were introduced to autism through a movie like "Rain Man," the 1988 film starring Dustin Hoffman as an autistic man with the mathematical skills of a savant; or perhaps by the TV series "Atypical," about a teenage boy with autism; or by the documentary film about Temple Grandin, an autistic woman who has famously contributed to animal science. These productions and many like them can aid our understanding of autism, but some also risk trivializing the subject. Still, the intersection of autism and the arts is a compelling one that not only serves to educate, but can at times provide those with autism with a form of therapy or with outlets for their own artistic expression.

The play, based on a novel by Mark Haddon, was a Tony winner on Broadway. In the Indiana-Syracuse production, Mickey Rowe, seated on the stage, made it a landmark for autistic actors.

Rowe joined with other cast members following a performance.

Early Thursday morning at the cafe across the street from Syracuse Stage, an actor named Mickey Rowe ducked in from the drizzly chill just as a barista unlocked the door. Starring as Christopher Boone in Simon Stephens's "The Curious Incident of the Dog in the Night-Time," he had a matinee to perform in a couple of hours, and an interview to give first.

On Broadway, where the play was a Tony Award-winning hit, it ran eight times a week, with two actors alternating the demanding role of Christopher, a 15-year-old with autism who sets out to solve a mystery. In Syracuse, Rowe — thought to be the first openly autistic actor to play the role — does all nine shows a week.

For him, such arduous work is a point of pride: evidence that an actor with a developmental disability can be up to the task. Confident enough in his performance to send a tweet to a writer for The New York Times, asking her to come and see (it worked), he means to show what's possible when companies take a chance on actors like him — and by extension, what's possible in the wider culture when other employers do.

He doesn't argue that roles like Christopher need to be played by people on the autism spectrum, but simply that those actors must be given a shot.

"I think it's theater's job to change the world," Rowe said over coffee. "I think it has a lot more power than it knows it has. And with that power comes great responsibility."

A boyish 29-year-old Seattle native with the slight but toned build of a gymnast, he looked me in the eye and shook my hand when we met. On our table, he placed a sheaf of papers face down — scripted notes it made him feel better to have, which he consulted if I asked a question he wanted to be careful answering. His vocal tone, timid at first, soon had the resonance of an actor's voice. "This is easy-ish for me because you're a reporter; I'm the interviewee," he said. "We have specific roles. If we met on the street, that would be more scary." That's how he's felt about performing, too, ever since he was little: perfectly comfortable as long as he knows the part he's meant to play.

Whether Rowe is the first autistic actor to play Christopher is hard to pin down, given the number of "Curious Incident" productions around the world. Even Simon Stephens, the playwright, said that while Rowe is the first he's heard of, he can't be sure.

Casting Rowe was the result of a deliberate effort by two professional regional theaters, Syracuse Stage and its co-producer, Indiana Repertory Theater (where the show opened in 2017), to audition actors both with and without autism for the role. At a time when theaters are discussing diversity, there is a heightened pressure to include performers with disabilities. "Uncommon Sense," Tectonic Theater Project's Off Broadway play about people with autism and their families, has an actor on the spectrum, Andrew Duff, in its ensemble.

The original version of this article appeared on Nov. 6, 2017. It has been edited for clarity and length.

Robert Hupp, the artistic director of Syracuse Stage, said that seeking out actors on the spectrum "made logical and irrefutable sense" for "Curious Incident." To him, Rowe's performance is clear validation.

"To anyone who ever had any concerns or doubts or wondered, 'Could an actor with autism play this role? Would an actor who falls on the spectrum be overwhelmed by this production?' the answer is definitively no," he said. "Not if you're Mickey Rowe."

Rowe, who earned a bachelor's degree in drama from the University of Washington, found out when he was a senior there that he had autism. Legally blind, he struggles to read print smaller than 18-point type (he wears contacts onstage and glasses "in real life," he says), and was in special education classes for his vision throughout childhood — years he spent friendless, obsessed with magic tricks and circus skills: stilt-walking, juggling, unicycling.

It strikes him as telling that he got speech and occupational therapy, too. He suspects his parents knew he had autism but didn't want to label him, and if so, he understands. He hasn't asked them, though; he said they don't have that kind of relationship.

It was his girlfriend — now his wife and the mother of their two small children — who urged him to get help with issues like interpreting social cues. At the university's Adult Autism Clinic, his diagnosis came as "a big relief, because you know your whole life that something is different," Rowe said. "You don't know why or what it is or if you're stupid or what's going on."

Still, he didn't tell people about his autism. So it was unsettling when, in an acting class he took around the time "Curious Incident" opened on Broadway in 2014, the teacher handed him one of Christopher's speeches and said, "You need to do this monologue. This is you."

"I remember thinking to myself afterward: Does she know I'm on the spectrum?" Rowe said. "Like, do people just know?"

He is not Christopher, though, and he and Christopher occupy very different spots on the spectrum. Even so, he recognized enough pieces of himself in that monologue that he went home and listened to the novel, by Mark Haddon, that Stephens adapted into the play.

Not long afterward, struggling to get work, Rowe threw in the towel on trying to pass as neurotypical. In an essay on the theater industry website HowlRound, he wrote about being an actor with autism, noting the "tension between everything that I am and everything that might be conventional for an actor." He hoped his disclosure would change the way people looked at him, just enough to give him a chance.

The piece raised his profile and put him on the radar of anyone searching for an actor with autism, but in practice nothing changed. Going out for roles, he still faced immediate roadblocks: the small talk, the eye contact, the instant connection an actor is supposed to make with the director.

"Just how you walk into the room and shake hands with the person when you first meet them is a huge part of the audition, and people on the spectrum aren't very good at that," he said.

So his résumé was comparatively slender when the Indiana-Syracuse production asked him to submit a video audition. Soon the show's California-based director, Risa Brainin, flew to Seattle to see if he had the chops. If he didn't, they weren't going to compromise.

"We couldn't," she said. "It's too major of a role, and too difficult of a role. What we wanted to do was give the opportunity."

In Syracuse, Rowe played Christopher with an agile grace, an impish humor and a humanizing restraint that seems directly connected to his experience of autism. When the stage directions said that Christopher barks like a dog, for example, Rowe chose to underplay it.

The attention the show has gotten has been positive for him. And the ripples extend farther. Marissa Wolf, who is directing "Curious Incident" at Kansas City Repertory Theater, said Rowe inspired her to choose an actor with Tourette's syndrome, a condition often associated with autism, to play Christopher in her production.

Rowe sees characters in the canon he thinks could be on the spectrum, like Bobby, the young misfit in David Mamet's play 'American Buffalo.'

Rowe worries about being pigeonholed, because he wants to play roles that have nothing to do with autism. Yet he also sees characters in the canon he thinks could be on the spectrum — like Bobby, the young misfit in David Mamet's "American Buffalo," and Jason, the awkward adolescent in David Lindsay-Abaire's "Rabbit Hole."

Eager to work with Rowe again, Hupp and Brainin have been scheming about future projects, pondering which roles — maybe something in Shakespeare? — would be a great fit for him.

What Mickey Rowe wants is a life in the American theater, probably with a stint in graduate school on the way. He can envision himself as the leader of a regional theater, and he is undaunted by the socializing that would require. Mingling may not be in his skill set, but to him, an artistic director is simply playing a role. And knowing that takes the fear away. ●

ESSAY

What a Muppet Means to My Family

The 'Sesame Street' character named Julia has autism. The lessons she teaches are valuable for autistic children, but perhaps even more so for neurotypical kids.

BY JENNIFER MALIA

Julia gives me hope that my children will grow up in a world where autism is normalized rather than stigmatized.

In "Meet Julia," an episode of "Sesame Street" that aired in 2017 on PBS and HBO, Elmo and Abby Cadabby introduce Big Bird to Julia, a new Muppet character with autism.

Big Bird says, "Hi, Julia, I'm Big Bird. Nice to meet you."

But Julia continues painting without making eye contact or responding to Big Bird. On "60 Minutes," Big Bird tells Lesley Stahl, who was on the set when "Sesame Street" was filming the new Muppet's debut, that he thought Julia didn't like him at first. Elmo then explains, "Julia has autism, so sometimes it takes her a little longer to do things."

I can relate.

When my daughter started preschool, she would run laps around the perimeter of the fenced-in playground without responding to kids who said "hi" as she passed by. One day, she stopped in her tracks to pick up a jacket that had fallen to the ground, handed it to a girl without saying a word, and continued running. The kids on the playground probably assumed she didn't like them — just as Big Bird did.

My daughter, who is now 3, my 2-year-old son and I were all given diagnoses of autism spectrum disorder because of our repetitive behaviors, obsessive interests, sensory issues and difficulty with social interactions and pragmatic communication skills. My kids are on the mild to moderate part of the spectrum, having language, but not intellectual, impairments. (I also have a daughter, age 4, who does not have a diagnosis.)

Julia gives me hope that my children and their peers will grow up in a world where autism is normalized, rather than stigmatized. Preschoolers are the primary audience for "Sesame Street," an educational program where young children watching Julia's interactions with her peers can learn by example to support autism acceptance. Since one in 68 American children have an autism diagnosis, wider understanding of the condition is valuable for them as well as for their peers.

Many people think of autism as affecting boys rather than girls, so simply presenting Julia, a female character, as the face of autism may help alter that perception. According to the Centers for Disease Control and Prevention, 4.5 boys are given the diagnosis for every girl. But according to new research on gender and autism, girls are often better than boys at masking their autistic traits as a coping mechanism, which may contribute to the skewed ratio.

"Sesame Street," which has tackled challenging subjects like racism and death, is now helping autism awareness become more mainstream. Like many parents of autistic kids from my generation, I was unknowingly hiding my autism until I recognized that I also had the autistic traits I saw in my daughter. I was in my late 30s when I was given a diagnosis of high-functioning autism spectrum disorder, without intellectual or language impairments — also labeled Asperger's syndrome. I want my kids to grow up knowing they're autistic, so they understand their differences better than I did.

Even as a child, I knew I was different. I was selectively mute, though at the time everyone thought I was just extremely shy. I didn't have many friends growing up because I didn't understand social communication, and this carried into my adult life. I don't want this kind of life for my kids.

I hope that having Julia as an accepted and likable character on "Sesame Street" will make it easier for my kids on the spectrum to navigate the social world.

My kids sometimes have meltdowns from the noise of jets passing overhead en route to the naval base near their preschool. "It's O.K., I'm here," I say to my kids, as other preschoolers and their parents walk by, staring at us huddled in the middle of the sidewalk.

So far my kids seem oblivious to the stares, but there may be a time when that changes. When kids watching "Sesame Street" witness Julia having a meltdown because of the sound of an ambulance siren, they'll see how her friends react.

The other Muppets try to comfort her, knowing that the noise bothers her, which helps to normalize meltdowns.

Elmo attempts to play "Peek-a-Boo" with Julia in Sesame Workshop's short video called "Julia's Bunny." When she doesn't respond immediately, he says, "We can play side by side like we do sometimes." Julia eventually ends up playing the game with Elmo, when she's ready. The same thing happens with my son. His preschool starts the day with unstructured play time. When I drop him off, I sit him down on the rug with a Little People farmhouse and animals, toys familiar to him. The other kids in his class come running over to play with him. Like Julia, he doesn't respond at first when one friend makes the pig "oink" at him, or another friend has the horse "neigh" at him, but eventually he picks up the cow and says, "moo," back at them.

Characters like Julia not only can serve as role models for kids who are on the spectrum, but also can help normalize autism for neurotypical kids. As the "Sesame Street" writer Christine Ferraro said on "60 Minutes," "I would love her to be not Julia, the kid on 'Sesame Street' who has autism. I would like her to be just Julia."

Me too. ●

The original version of this article appeared on April 7, 2017. It has been edited for clarity and length. Jennifer Malia is an associate professor of English at Norfolk State University and the author of "Too Sticky! Sensory Issues With Autism."

ESSAY

The Trouble With Autism in Novels

Novelists have often chosen to use (and misuse) autism as a metaphor for other things. For a writer with an autistic son, this seems a disservice.

BY MARIE MYUNG-OK LEE

I read every night to my teenage son, who has severe autism. Only recently has he been calm enough to tolerate this, but it's become an enjoyable ritual. I'm not sure what he understands, yet as I read Helen Macdonald's memoir, "H Is for Hawk," about a woman's year of grief and falconry, J gets a dreamy look on his face. On nights he's worried I'll forget, he'll come to me and demand: "Read bird hawk!"

As a teacher, book columnist and novelist, I'm something of a professional reader. Casting about for what to read to J next, I've noticed a surge of books with autism in them. I don't mean books about autism, but, rather, novels that include characters who have autism or that use symptoms of the disorder as a metaphor or plot device, or to stylize language.

These portrayals drove me to revisit "Illness as Metaphor" (1978), Susan Sontag's critical look at the "literary transfiguration" of illness. Tuberculosis, a microbial infection characterized by sputum and wracking coughs, became the "romantic disease" of the 19th century, its fevers and pallor standing in for creativity, beauty and moral superiority. Novels of the era were populated with beautiful TB deaths whenever an innocent deserved a peaceful and painless end, perhaps most memorably Little Eva in "Uncle Tom's Cabin."

With the virtual eradication of tuberculosis in the 20th century, it receded as a dominant form of illness — in art as in life. Cancer filled the void, but with darker metaphors of shame, external disfigurement, war. Like cancer and like TB before the discovery of the mycobacterium tuberculosis, autism is a condition whose etiology remains largely a mystery.

Bruno Bettelheim, in his influential book "The Empty Fortress: Infantile Autism and the Birth of the Self" (1967), famously blamed the disorder on emotionally frigid "refrigerator mothers," and doctors recommended that children with autism be separated from their mothers and institutionalized.

Sontag concluded that the truest way to portray illness was without metaphor, and it might seem that Bettelheim was writing in the metaphor-free space of observational science. But though his publishers touted him as a child psychologist, he had no credentials other than having attended three introductory classes in the field.

Vestiges of the "refrigerator mother" metaphor continue in literature. Cormac McCarthy's postapocalyptic novel "The Road" (2006) takes place in a "cold autistic dark." The narrator of Jonathan Lethem's novel "The Fortress of Solitude" (2003) compares himself with his childhood friend Arthur: "It was a form of autism, a failure at social mimicry that had kept me from the adaptations which made Arthur more Brooklyn than me. . . . I'd had to hide in books, Manhattanize." Lethem has cited autism as a source of literary inspiration: "It's evocative for me. I'm enticed by it."

The original version of this article appeared on Feb. 10, 2019. It has been edited for clarity and length. Marie Myung-Ok Lee is a novelist who teaches fiction writing at Columbia.

With autism there is often, not metaphorically but literally, a lack of voice, which renders the person a tabula rasa on which a writer can inscribe almost anything.

More recently, in Don DeLillo's "Zero K" (2016), a near-future novel about the attempt of the hyper-rich to attain eternal life, a character named Jeffrey observes a class of special-needs children: "The boy at the end of the table who can't produce the specific motor movements that would allow him to speak words that others might understand" and "the girl who could not take a step without sensing some predetermined danger," adding, in a nod to Sontag, "She was not a metaphor." And yet the end of the novel features a presumably autistic child pressed into metaphoric duty, when the same character, riding a New York City bus at dusk, watches a boy repetitively bouncing in time to "prelinguistic grunts" and "howls." As the sun's last rays illuminate the columns of skyscrapers, Jeffrey reflects: "I didn't need heaven's light. I had the boy's cries of wonder."

Thus autism becomes a metaphor for higher human understanding, a transcendent plane beyond language.

That autism explodes the conventional American nuclear family narrative makes it irresistible as a metaphor for the stresses of life under late-stage capitalism. In Helen Schulman's "A Day at the Beach" (2007), a wealthy Manhattan couple navigate the worst day of their lives: the 9/11 disaster, which causes them to flee their swank downtown home (to the Hamptons) and strains their marriage — already at the breaking point owing to a son who shows clear signs of autism. In Gary Shteyngart's "Lake Success" (2018), a son's autism diagnosis similarly destroys an elite Manhattan family's dreams.

Like TB and cancer before it, autism can accumulate moral weight. In Louise Erdrich's "Four Souls" (2004), a white settler who has despoiled the Minnesota pine forests and cheated its Ojibwe inhabitants subsequently endures the immolation of his business empire as well as the birth of a son with "vacant" eyes, "the very picture of idiocy," who makes "hideous" sounds and cannot be "soothed out of his gross repetition." Here is the transfiguration of a neurobiological disease into one that lays waste to the mind, taking along with it all the qualities that make us human.

I ask myself why using autism the way these books do feels wrong. As a child who was disappointed to find the only Asian characters in any book in the library to be the Japanese-American family in "Farewell to Manzanar," I am acutely aware of the importance of feeling represented in literature. And yet, when it comes to autism appearing in literary fiction, I instinctively feel a need to protect my son from these portrayals. He's not an Ojibwe curse, a savant or an alien. Nor is he an emotionless cipher with no inner life.

As a writer, I understand the absurdity of trying to place restrictions on what can and can't be written about.

The crux of the issue is that with autism there is often, not metaphorically but literally, a lack of voice, which renders the person a tabula rasa on which a writer can inscribe and project almost anything: Autism is a gift, a curse, super intelligence, mental retardation, mystical, repellent, morally edifying, a parent's worst nightmare. As a writer, I say go ahead and write what you want. As a parent, I find this terrifying, given the way neurotypical people project false motives and feelings onto the actions of others every day.

With this divided consciousness, I am endlessly appreciative of "The Reason I Jump" (2013), a book by Naoki Higashida, a Japanese man with autism who is nonverbal and beset by behaviors that would, by conventional standards, cause him to be labeled, like my son, "low-functioning."

Higashida's mother created a special alphabet grid that eventually allowed her son to communicate by pointing. While still a teenager, he wrote "The Reason I Jump," describing what it feels like to have autism.

The book made its way to the English-speaking world after being discovered and translated from the Japanese by the novelist David Mitchell and his wife, KA Yoshida, who have a son with autism. Mitchell wrote that "'The Reason I Jump' consolidated my wife's and my suspicions that, in fact, people with autism feel what everyone else does. They just cannot show they feel it." This book is a single author's perspective, not a textbook, but I'm grateful for Higashida's hard-won voice: "You can't judge a person by their looks. But once you know the other person's inner self, both of you can be that much closer. From your point of view, the world of autism must look like a deeply mysterious place. So please, spare a little time to listen to what I have to say."

My son, J, has a beautiful, warm smile. He also screams and barks for no particular reason I can discern. He laughs loudly at "inappropriate" times. He repetitively jumps up and down and calls it "dancing." He has hit and bit me, and hit himself as well. His disordered language is a neurological effect, not a tendency toward gnomic utterances. The dysfunction of the mirror neurons in his brain does not render him a Lethemesque "failure at social mimicry." The noise and stress of ordinary conversation can cause him to shut down, yet I would never say that he is cold or lacks emotions or prefers to stay inside himself.

I don't know what J is thinking, but I know that he *is* thinking. Now that my son appears to enjoy it when I read to him, I hope to introduce him to a wide variety of books, being mindful to avoid those that reduce his experience — and, by extension, him — to a literary construct. ●

BOOK REVIEW

A Family Memoir Makes the Case That Autism Is Different, Not Less

BY RON SUSKIND

In just the third paragraph of what turns into an uncommonly riotous and moving book, Judith Newman dives headlong into the highly charged debate over whether to replace the term "autistic" with more cautious, politically correct language: "a man with autism, a woman with autism."

Newman understands the impulse behind such "person-first" nomenclature, but she's not buying it. The phrase "person with autism," she writes, "suggests that autism is something bad that one needs distance from. You'd never say 'a person with left-handedness' or 'a person with Jewishness.' Then again, you might say a 'person with cancer.' . . . There's also something about this pseudo-delicacy that is patronizing as hell."

What follows in "To Siri With Love: A Mother, Her Autistic Son, and the Kindness of Machines," are 200 pages of powerfully wrought indelicacies about life with Gus, her autistic teenage son, that will make readers squirm and laugh — yes, out loud. Newman will also make them face questions everyone's ducking (vasectomies for autistic men?) before sweeping them, finally, into a soul-spilling high tide.

Gus has the good fortune to be born into a family of eccentrics — a character among characters — led by Judith, an only child who grew up with pet iguanas, knew dogs better than children, got married at 30 to John, a 60-year-old divorced British opera singer who doesn't like mess or noise.

They produced a set of fraternal twins in Henry and Gus, setting up quickly apparent distinctions between a typically developing, hyper-precocious child and his "delayed" brother, whose troubling deficits they managed

The original version of this article appeared on Aug. 16, 2017. Ron Suskind is a Pulitzer Prize-winning journalist and author and the founder of Sidekicks, a builder of augmentative technologies.

to deny creatively for years. A columnist for the Book Review, Newman is courageous in exposing herself and ingenious in enlisting every feature of her family life to show that autistic people, like the rest of the Newman ensemble, are different, not less.

Autism memoirs are generally written from one of two perspectives, person with or parent of, and Newman's is among the best of the parenting breed. As she removes the zone of privacy from herself and her family, she is edging into the world her son occupies. Those with autism often say whatever is on their mind — no filter — and have difficulty lying even when it's in their self-interest. In this way, Newman the writer becomes autistic, and ends up serving the interest of the reader.

That reader is privy to the family's long years working on language attainment with Gus, who, as Newman points out, is an "average" autistic kid — by far the majority, squarely between the poles of "the eccentric genius who will one day be running NASA!" and "the person so impaired he is smashing his head against the wall and finger painting with the blood."

Yet Newman is no dogmatist who celebrates every difference as a delight and inalienable right. In some of the book's hardest-eyed passages, she writes about how much Gus will never do, and shouldn't, including reproducing: "It is very hard to say this out loud. Let me try. I do not want Gus to have children."

The book's title is drawn directly from a New York Times article Newman wrote in 2014 about Gus's bond with Siri, Apple's "intelligent personal assistant," who could endlessly answer his questions, keep her son company and express the gift of common courtesy. Does it dehumanize us if tenderness is tried out first with a machine? While his hyper-aware twin is showing standard bright-future achievements, Gus tentatively feels his way through life. But make no mistake. Gus's deft fingers — rendered with unsentimental affection by his mom—are feeling things others will miss.

At one point, Gus says, "Good night, Siri, will you sleep well tonight?" Siri replies: "I don't need much sleep, but it's nice of you to ask."

Newman's response could speak for the entire book: "Very nice."

TO SIRI WITH LOVE
Judith Newman's memoir is a moving yet surprisingly funny and sharp-edged chronicle of her eccentric family and the life of her autistic son, Gus.

BOOK EXCERPT

Reaching My Son Through Disney

BY RON SUSKIND

In our first year in Washington, our son disappeared. Just shy of his 3rd birthday, an engaged, chatty child, full of typical speech — "I love you," "Where are my Ninja Turtles?" "Let's get ice cream!" — fell silent. He cried, inconsolably. Didn't sleep. Wouldn't make eye contact. His only word was "juice." ¶ I had just started a job as The Wall Street Journal's national affairs reporter. My wife, Cornelia, a former journalist, was home with him — a new story every day, a new horror. He could barely use a sippy cup, though he'd long ago graduated to a big-boy cup. He wove about like someone walking with his eyes shut. "It doesn't make sense," I'd say at night. "You don't grow backward." Had he been injured somehow when he was out of our sight, banged his head, swallowed something poisonous? It was like searching for clues to a kidnapping. ¶ After visits to several doctors, we first

The original version of this article appeared on March 9, 2014. It has been edited for clarity and length, and was adapted from Ron Suskind's book "Life, Animated."

A 12-year-old Owen at Walt Disney World.

heard the word "autism." Later, it would be fine-tuned to "regressive autism," now affecting roughly a third of children with the disorder. Unlike the kids born with it, this group seems typical until somewhere between 18 and 36 months — then they vanish. Some never get their speech back. Families stop watching those early videos, their child waving to the camera. Too painful. That child's gone.

In the year since his diagnosis, Owen's only activity with his brother, Walt, is something they did before the autism struck: watching Disney movies. "The Little Mermaid," "Beauty and the Beast," "Aladdin" — it was a boom time for Disney — and also the old classics: "Dumbo," "Fantasia," "Pinocchio," "Bambi." They watch on a television bracketed to a high corner of our bedroom in Georgetown. It is hard to know all the things going through the mind of our 6-year-old, Walt, about how his little brother, now nearly 4, is changing.

They pile up pillows on our bed and sit close, Walt often with his arm around Owen's shoulders, trying to hold him — and the shifting world — in place.

Then Walt slips out to play with friends, and Owen keeps watching. Movie after movie. Certain parts he rewinds and rewatches. Lots of rewinding. But he seems content, focused.

We ask our growing team of developmental specialists, doctors and therapists about it. We were never big fans of plopping our kids in front of Disney videos, but now the question seemed more urgent: Is this good for him? They shrug. Is he relaxed? Yes. Does it seem joyful? Definitely. Keep it limited, they say. But if it does all that for him, there's no reason to stop it.

So we join him upstairs, all of us, on a cold and rainy Saturday afternoon in November 1994. Owen is already on the bed, oblivious to our arrival, murmuring gibberish: "Juicervose, juicervose." It is something we've been hearing for the past few weeks. Cornelia thinks maybe he wants more juice; but no, he refuses the sippy cup. "The Little Mermaid" is playing as we settle in, propping up pillows. We've all seen it at least a dozen times, but it's at one of the best parts: where Ursula the sea witch, an acerbic diva, sings her song of villainy, "Poor Unfortunate Souls," to the selfish mermaid, Ariel, setting up the part in which Ursula will turn Ariel into a human, allowing her to seek out the handsome prince, in exchange for her voice.

When the song is over, Owen lifts the remote. Hits rewind.

"Come on, Owen, just let it play!" Walt moans. But Owen goes back just 20 seconds or so, to the song's next-to-last stanza, with Ursula shouting:

Go ahead — make your choice!

I'm a very busy woman, and I haven't got all day.

It won't cost much, just your voice!

He does it again. Stop. Rewind. Play. And one more time. On the fourth pass, Cornelia whispers, "It's not 'juice.'" I barely hear her. "What?" "It's not 'juice.' It's 'just' . . . 'just your voice'!"

I turn and grab Owen by the shoulders. "Just your voice! Is that what you're saying?!"

From left: Owen at 18 months, before signs of autism, and at age 3, just after symptoms developed.

He looks right at me, our first real eye contact in a year. "Juicervose! Juicervose! Juicervose!"

Walt starts to shout, "Owen's talking again!" A mermaid lost her voice in a moment of transformation. So did this silent boy. "Juicervose! Juicervose! Juicervose!" Owen keeps saying it, watching us shout and cheer. And then we're up, all of us, bouncing on the bed. Owen, too, singing it over and over — "Juicervose!" — as Cornelia, tears beginning to fall, whispers softly, "Thank God, he's in there."

We told his various therapists about what happened. Cornelia and I could think of little else. Owen reached out, if only for a moment, from his shut-in world. We spoke to our child.

The speech therapist tamped down our enthusiasm. Dr. Alan Rosenblatt, our trusted developmental pediatrician, did, too. He explained that echolalia is a common feature in kids like Owen. It's something babies sometimes do between 6 and 9 months, repeating consonants and vowels as they learn to turn babble into words. It's also something seen in people with developmental disabilities who can't speak. Just like what the term suggests, they echo, usually the last word or two of a sentence. "You're a very smart and pretty girl," a mother might say to her daughter. "Pretty girl," the child will respond, an echo. Do those kids know what the words mean, we pressed Rosenblatt. "Usually not," he said. "They may want to make a connection, which is hopeful," he added.

"They just repeat the last sound," I croaked. He nodded. Why, I persisted, in a last stab, would he be rewinding that one part for weeks, maybe longer, and choose that phrase from so many in an 83-minute movie? Rosenblatt shrugged. No way of knowing.

Three weeks after the "juicervose" dance, we are at Walt Disney World. Walt grabs Owen's hand, and off they go down Main Street, U.S.A. There are attractions in Fantasyland — the Mad Tea Party, Snow White's Scary Adventures, Mr. Toad's Wild Ride — that echo movies they both love. The boys sit in the flying galleon on Peter Pan's Flight as it swirls and dips over landscapes and figures from Never Land, the Lost Boys frolicking in their lair, Wendy walking the plank, Peter Pan crossing swords with Captain Hook. They look like any other pair of brothers, and in the trick of this light, they are.

Each time Cornelia and I feel that, we catch ourselves. After the "juicervose" euphoria and then the cold water poured on us by doctors, we try to make sure we aren't just seeing what we want to see.

But by midafternoon, it's clear that Owen isn't self-talking in the streams of gibberish or flapping his hands as he usually does. Some, but not much. He seems calm and focused — following the group, making eye contact — and oddly settled, with a slight smile, eyes alight, just as he is while watching the movies on our bed. Owen seems at home here, as though his identity, or however much of it has formed, is somehow tied to this place.

It's Walt's 9th birthday, September 1997, in our new house near Chevy Chase Circle. Owen is 6½. After roughhousing with buddies in the backyard at the end of his party, Walt gets a little weepy. He's already a tough, independent kid, often the case with siblings of disabled kids. But he can get a little sad on his birthdays. As Cornelia and I return to the kitchen, Owen walks in right behind us.

He looks intently at us, one, then the other. "Walter doesn't want to grow up," he says evenly, "like Mowgli or Peter Pan."

We nod, dumbly, looking down at him. He nods back and then vanishes into some private reverie.

It's as if a thunderbolt just passed through the kitchen. A full sentence, and not just an "I want this" or "Give me that." No, a complex sentence, the likes of which he'd not uttered in four years. Actually, ever.

We don't say anything at first and then don't stop talking for the next four hours, peeling apart, layer by layer, what just happened. Beyond the language, it's interpretive thinking that he's not supposed to be able to do: that someone crying on his birthday may not want to grow up. Not only would such an insight be improbable for a typical 6-year-old; it was an elegant connection that Cornelia and I overlooked.

It's as if Owen had let us in, just for an instant, to glimpse a mysterious grid growing inside him, a matrix on which he affixed items he saw each day that we might not even notice. And then he carefully aligned it to another one, standing parallel: The world of Disney.

After dinner is over and the boys retreat upstairs to their attic lair, Cornelia starts to think about what to do now. It's like he peeked out from some vast underground and then vanished. He's done this before, but never quite like this. "How on earth," she says almost to herself, "do you get back in there?"

I feel she's asking me. She has been the one lifting the burden each day, driving him to therapists and schools, rocking him to sleep as he thrashes at 3 a.m. I'm the one who tells stories, does voices. Her look says, "Find a way."

Soon I'm tiptoeing up the carpeted stairs. Owen's sitting on his bed, flipping through a Disney book; he can't read, of course, but he likes to look at the pictures. The mission is to reach around the banister into his closet and grab his puppet of Iago, the parrot from "Aladdin" and one of his favorite characters. Once Iago's in hand, I gently pull the bedspread from the foot of Owen's bed onto the floor. He doesn't look up. It takes four minutes for Iago and me to make it safely under the bedspread.

Now crawl, snail-slow, along the side of the bed to its midpoint. Fine.

I freeze here for a minute, trying to figure out my opening line; four or five sentences dance about, auditioning.

Then, a thought: *Be* Iago. What would Iago say? I push the puppet up from the covers. "So, Owen, how ya doin'?" I say, doing my best Iago voice. "I mean, how does it feel to be you?!" I can see him turn toward Iago. It's as if he is bumping into an old friend. "I'm not happy. I don't have friends. I can't understand what people say." I have not heard this voice, natural and easy, with the traditional rhythm of common speech, since he was 2. I'm talking to my son for the first time in five years. Or Iago is. *Stay in character.* "So, Owen, when did *yoooou* and I become such good friends?"

"When I started watching 'Aladdin' all the time. You made me laugh so much. You're so funny."

My mind is racing — find a snatch of dialogue, anything. One scene I've seen him watch and rewind is when Iago tells the villainous vizier Jafar how he should become sultan.

Back as Iago: "Funny? O.K., Owen, like when I say . . . um. So, so, you marry the princess and you become the chump husband." Owen makes a gravelly sound, like someone trying to clear his throat or find a lower tone: "I *loooove* the way your fowl little mind works." It's a Jafar line, in Jafar's voice — a bit higher-pitched, of course, but all there, the faintly British accent, the sinister tone.

I'm an evil parrot talking to a Disney villain, and he's talking back. Then, I hear a laugh, a joyful little laugh that I have not heard in many years.

A week after the Iago breakthrough, we decide to try an experiment. Owen usually picks the animated movie whenever we gather in front of the 26-inch Magnavox in the basement. On this night, we pick it for him: "The Jungle Book." It's a movie that the boys have long loved and one that Cornelia and I remember from our childhood: Disney's 1967 rendition of Rudyard Kipling's tales of Mowgli, a boy raised by wolves in the jungles of India, schooled by Baloo, the obstreperous bear, and Bagheera, the protective black panther.

We watch the movie until, a few minutes along, Baloo looks at Mowgli; I look at Owen and he looks squarely back at me, and then it happens. Right on cue, he says, "'You eat ants?'" That's Mowgli's line; he speaks it as Mowgli, almost like a tape recording.

I'm poised with Baloo's next line: "'Ha-ha, you better believe it! And you're gonna love the way they tickle.'"

A few minutes later, when King Louie, the crazy orangutan, voiced by the jazz trumpeter and singer Louis Prima, sings to Mowgli about becoming a man, Walt's ready. "'Teach me the secret of man's red fire,'" he says, pulling on his ear, waiting for the whispered secret from the boy. Owen recoils, just as Mowgli does in the movie, and says, "'I don't know how to make fire.'" Cornelia catches my eye; I shake my head. The inflection and ease of speech are things he can't otherwise muster. It's almost as though there's no autism. Mimicry is one thing. This isn't that. The movements, the tone, the emotions seem utterly authentic, like method acting.

Owen gets this look where he raises his eyebrows and presses his face into the widest of smiles. He calls it 'happy face.' He does it when he's worried that he might start to cry.

So begin the basement sessions. During daylight, we go about our lives. Walt rides his bike to school each morning, back home each afternoon. Cornelia manages the house, the bills, the overloaded schedules of the kids. I am editing and writing for The Journal, putting on my suit and subwaying to the bureau. No one knows we're all living double lives. At night, we become animated characters.

By the fall of 1999, the start of Owen's third year at the Lab School of Washington, a private school for kids with learning disabilities, we see his skills improving, his rudimentary reading, his new ability to do simple math. But the progress is uneven and unsteady, as is the building of social connections with potential friends. It's a struggle for him to keep up, the school warns us darkly, because his mind so often races through the parallel universe of movies.

By his fifth year at Lab, we sense trouble has arrived. Owen is making progress, but the other kids, with lighter burdens, are moving faster. Sally Smith, the school's director, says it just isn't working out for Owen at Lab. What we both know is that the school has changed. "Look, I'm sorry," she says quietly. "Times change. We're serving a need and serving it well. Just not anymore for someone like Owen."

We call the school he was at six years before, Ivymount, which is for needier and more disabled kids. They're sympathetic and say they will gladly take him back. We're worried that he'll lose some of the gains he has made, but we don't have much of a choice.

We tell Owen in early May 2002, a month before he will leave his school. We go out to dinner and say he'll be going back to Ivymount. He has made a few friends at Lab. They do things together, are starting to form little rituals. "It'll be great, Owie," Walt says, putting his arm around Owen's shoulder. Owen gets this look where he raises his eyebrows and presses his face into the widest of smiles. He calls it "happy face." He does it when he's worried he might cry.

Back at Ivymount in the fall, Owen, now 11, is not being challenged academically or socially. All he wants are sketch pads and pencils. Markers, too. He goes through a pad in a few days and wants another. O.K., back to the CVS. A few more days, he needs another one. I look around for what are now two missing pads. They're nowhere. Could he have hidden them?

One Saturday afternoon, I see Owen padding across the kitchen's Mexican tile floor on his way to the basement with pad, pencils and one of his large animation books in hand. I wait a minute before I tiptoe behind him, stopping at the bottom of the stairs. He's on the rug, kneeling but hunched forward, flipping furiously through the book; as I edge closer, I see it contains artwork from "Learn to Draw Disney's The Little Mermaid."

Standing silently over him, I can see he's stopping at pictures of Sebastian, the wise crab who watches over the heroine, Ariel. There are lots of Sebastians: pencil sketches from when the animators were developing the character, full-color renderings of key scenes from the movie. That is where he stops, at a slide of Sebastian with a fearful look, mouth open and eyes wide.

The sketchbook flies open, the black pencil in hand. He looks from the picture to his pad, picture, pad, picture, pad. And then the tightly gripped pencil begins to move, a lead-lined crawl. Most kids, most anyone, would begin with the face — where we all tend to look first — but he starts on the edge, with the crab leg, then the claw, which take shape in a single line. But here's the crazy part: Every part of him starts moving except that rock-steady hand. His whole body begins twisting and flinching, moving as much as you can move while kneeling, with his free arm bending in the angle of Sebastian's left claw. Five minutes later, when he gets to the face, I look up and see a reflection of Owen's face, me behind him, in the darkened screen of the TV in front of us. The look on the crab's face in the book is replicated in my son's reflection on the TV, where, of course, we've watched this scene — of Sebastian watching Ariel lose her voice — so many times.

A drawing by Owen of Abu from "Aladdin."

And then it's over, like a passing storm. He drops the pencil, rears back, turns his head, leaps up and bounds off.

It freaks me out.

He can't write his name legibly. But here is a rendering of a Disney character that might have easily appeared in any one of 20 animation books in his room.

I squat down and begin flipping. It's one character after another — the Mad Hatter next to Rafiki, and then Lumiere, the candelabra from "Beauty and the Beast," and then Jiminy Cricket. The expressions are all so vivid, mostly fearful. Dozens of them, page after page.

I settle in cross-legged on the carpet to examine the pages. What do the drawings mean? Are the faces of these characters a reflection of hidden, repressed feelings? Does he race through the books looking for an expression that matches the way he feels and then literally draw that emotion to the surface?

Could be a half-hour I'm sitting, maybe longer. I'm inside him, or so I imagine, running my fingers along the slight indentations of carbon — a smiling mouth of Baloo, a weeping dwarf, a soaring crow from "Dumbo" — to try to touch him, his tears and smiles and moments of sudden flight. This is the crushing pain of autism. Of not being able to know your own child, to share love and laughter with him, to comfort him, to answer his questions. Cornelia spends time in here, in his head — this

The Suskind family in 1996. From left, Cornelia, Walt, Owen and Ron.

child she carried — whispering to him. Now I'm in here, too.

Time passes, pages turn. And then I see writing. On the next to last page of the sketchbook, there's something. It's his usual scrawl, the letters barely legible: "I Am the Protekter of Sidekicks."

I flip to the last page. In the chicken scratch of a kindergartner is a single sentence: "No Sidekick Gets Left Behind."

We need the right moment to respond. Every second we're with Owen in the coming days, Cornelia and I look for our opening — a moment when he's alone, or settled, or upbeat or a bit more talkative than usual. Then the stars align. He's watching "Beauty and the Beast" and wants us all to join him. Soon we're together in the basement, watching the familiar opening, when the handsome prince spurns an old, ugly woman on a forbidding night, only to have her transform into a beautiful enchantress, who turns him into a hideous beast; a spell that can be broken only if he can "learn to love another and earn her love in return."

As the credits roll, we do a few voices — I say, "Sacre bleu, invaders!" as Lumiere. Cornelia throws in Mrs. Potts: "He's finally learned to love." Owen rises to each with a burst of follow-up lines. We respond in character. "They're a great pair of . . . sidekicks," Cornelia says. We've never used the word with him in conversation. Owen snaps to. "I love Mrs. Potts and Lumiere," he says.

"What is a sidekick?" Cornelia asks him.

"A sidekick helps the hero fulfill his destiny," he chirps. Rolls right off his tongue. A classical, elegant definition.

"Do you feel like a sidekick, Owie?" Cornelia asks him softly. Their eyes are aligned, just the two of them now, looking into each other, until he suddenly breaks into "happy face."

"I am one!" he says. His voice is high and cheery, no sign of a quaver. "I am a sidekick." The words come out flat, without affectation. But he compensates, giving them expression by nodding after every two syllables.

"And no . . . sidekick . . . gets left . . . behind."

There's no doubt, now, that he sees what we see: that kids of all kinds are moving on, while he's left behind. The sidekicks have emerged, sketch by sketch, in the difficult months since his ejection from Lab. His response has been to embrace it, the pain of it, and be a protector of the discarded. He starts giving sidekick identities to his classmates at Ivymount, so many of whom are heavily burdened — some with physical infirmities, and plenty of autistic kids with little speech. But they have qualities that he's identifying — this one was loyal, that one gentle, another one silly in some lighthearted way that makes him laugh.

It's often the supporting players in Disney fables who are more varied and vivid. Even in the earliest Disney movies, the first sidekicks — Goofy, Pluto and then Donald Duck — often carried confusions, frailties, foolishness, pride, vanity and hard-won, often reluctantly learned, insights. The spectrum of complex human emotions is housed with the sidekicks.

Owen and I walk gingerly down the icy steps of a side entrance to Dan Griffin's basement office in Takoma Park, Md. It's a particularly cold and stormy afternoon in December 2005, the week before Christmas. Griffin welcomes us with hugs, as always, and we settle into our usual chairs.

Owen started seeing the psychologist last year, when he was 13. More than any other therapist, Griffin took to the "Disney therapy," or more broadly, what might be called "affinity therapy," that Cornelia and I, with Walt's assistance, have been conducting for years in our home, and even more so recently.

Like many other therapists we'd seen, Griffin was initially a little concerned about Owen's intense affinity for Disney movies — but unlike the others, he became intrigued. In fact, he had come up with an ingenious plan for Owen to protect and advise a sidekick. We had settled on Zazu, the proud but naïve hornbill charged with protecting a young Simba in "The Lion King." Owen said, "Zazu has a lot to learn."

Hence:

Educating Zazu

I, Owen Harry Suskind, agree to undertake the challenging but critical task of providing stimulating educational experiences for my good friend Zazu. This project will take a good deal of work and preparation, but should be a lot of fun and also immensely beneficial to Zazu. I agree to do this for the academic year of 2005–6.

We start today's therapy session in December with talk of Zazu and his progress. The focus is on making friends.

Owen doesn't have friends, other than kids he encounters through carefully structured activities. But when advising Zazu, Owen suddenly seems full of advice about how to make friends.

"To make a friend, you have to be a friend," he says, picking up a line that is used at Walt's summer camp; it's something Cornelia has said to him a few times but has never heard him repeat. "And you need to be interested in what they're interested in," Owen adds. "And then they can be interested in what you're interested in."

Owen seems to infuse the advice with feeling. Instead of just repeating these chestnuts about social skills, he seems to be really owning them. Griffin — whom Owen has dubbed Rafiki, after the wise baboon in "The Lion King" — keeps up the momentum by mentioning the "second-question rule" for keeping a conversation going, asking narrower questions: "When did you do that? Who else was with you? How did that feel?" We practice a few of those, all three of us.

Owen mentions how Zazu has trouble with one of his lessons — loving people — because he's "ashamed about how he failed Simba," who slipped away and got into trouble — trouble that eventually led to his father's death.

Griffin takes the risk of asking Owen to elaborate about the fairly complex dynamic between Zazu and Simba; when you fail to meet your own expectations and disappoint someone you care about, what does that feel like? As Owen is thinking, I mouth "P-h-i-l" to Griffin. He knows immediately which scene I'm thinking of and asks Owen if this is what happens to Phil in "Hercules."

Owen starts to laugh. "Can I do it?"

Before we can nod, Owen's off and running, doing a scene in which Phil is trying to tell a crowd of doubters about Hercules's potential. We watch as Owen seems to access the emotions of Phil, Hercules and the three other characters in that scene. He ends with a plea from Hercules: "How am I supposed to prove myself a hero if nobody will give me a chance?"

As the session ends, Griffin pulls me aside. "Autistic kids like Owen are not supposed to do that," he says. "This is getting weird in a very good way."

What we're hoping to get our arms around one night in 2010, just before Owen is to graduate from high school, is some sense of what the future — the long future — might look like.

There's a knock on our door, and Team Owen begins to arrive. Griffin, the psychologist, is excited to see Dr. Lance Clawson, the psychiatrist; they've never met, though they've exchanged reports on Owen and other patients they share. Suzie Blattner, an education specialist, has been tutoring Owen since he was 3, right around the time Bill Stixrud, his neuropsychological testing specialist, first tested him. That's 15 years. These people have helped Cornelia and me parent our son. It's a humbling thought, and one that prompts a blurring of lines between hired professional and friend.

The immediate issue is what comes next, how the autistic world and the "neurotypical" world might be fitted together for Owen.

But over the hour and into the next, Griffin talks more and more about Owen's progress with the Disney therapy, as we've come to call it. Of course everyone knows of his affinity for these movies, as it has been a factor in the work of every one of them. For the first time, though, we can hear them discuss, professional to professional, what's been going on in Griffin's office.

"It's not so much how he's used the movies to help with academics," Blattner says. "It's how he's used them to guide emotional growth, which, of course, is the bigger and more complex challenge."

Everyone nods to that.

Griffin cites some surprising recent breakthroughs. Owen has been whispering under his breath to sidekicks for years, having them guide him as he faces challenges. He is developing a version of "inner speech," something that typical people develop as children to "think through" behavior and plan actions, the core cognitive processes of executive function, which are thought to be deficient in autistic people. Lately, Owen has let us in on it. At our prompting, he tells us how various sidekicks would solve his problems, quell his fears. He does it in the characters' voices, seeming to channel insights that are otherwise inaccessible to him.

Griffin tells the group how he has recently channeled Rafiki's voice on why change is so hard and how we manage it, and Jiminy Cricket's on the meaning of conscience and how to converse with that "voice in your head."

Owen, now 20, is opening the microwave in the galley kitchen when we arrive at Riverview, a school on Cape Cod, one day in April 2012. "Should I put in the Orville's?" he calls to the dorm counselor out in the suite, gets the O.K. and then emerges to help us lay out cups, juice and M&M's on a table in the TV lounge. The students trickle in.

It's the Sunday-night meeting of Disney Club. Owen decided to start the group not long after he arrived at Riverview eight months ago. It has been a fine first year so far in their college program: He's getting a mix of academic and social challenges, has made one good friend and is building independence.

Starting Disney Club has been a highlight; he has never been a member of a club, never mind the president of one. About a dozen students come to Owen's dorm each week, settle in to eat popcorn, chat a bit and watch their favorites. A few times he described club meetings to us, and we tried to suggest activities over the phone. Then a few weeks ago, he asked if we could come out as Disney Club's parent advisers.

We always knew there were other autism-spectrum kids who focused intently on Disney — we'd met several, after all, over the years. But by starting this club, Owen has drawn together a roomful of them.

Tonight's selection is "Dumbo," a fertile tale of self-recognition and emergence. After we watch a bit of the movie, we pause it and talk about how the thing that makes the little elephant a pariah, his huge ears, ultimately allows him to soar. I ask each of them about their "hidden ears," the thing "that makes them different — maybe even an outcast — that they've discovered is a great strength."

The room gets quiet. It's clear that many of these students have rarely, if ever, had their passion for Disney treated as something serious and meaningful.

There's a reason that each autistic person has embraced a particular interest. Find that reason and you will find them, hiding in there. As the Disney Club members say, it's about 'finding the hidden ears.'

One young woman talks about how her gentle nature, something that leaves her vulnerable, is a great strength in how she handles rescue dogs. Another mentions "my brain, because it can take me on adventures of imagination."

A young man, speaking in a very routinized way with speech patterns that closely match the "Rain Man" characterization of autism, asks me the date of my birth. I tell him, and his eyes flicker. "That was a Friday."

When I ask the group which Disney character they most identify with, the same student, now enlivened, says Pinocchio and eventually explains, "I feel like a wooden boy, and I've always dreamed of feeling what real boys feel." The dorm counselor, who told me ahead of time that this student has disciplinary issues and an unreachable emotional core, then compliments him — "That was beautiful," she says — and looks at me with astonishment. I shrug. He'd already bonded in a soul-searching way with his character. I just asked him which one.

It goes on this way for an hour. Like a broken dam. The students, many of whom have very modest expressive speech, summon subtle and deeply moving truths.

There's a reason — a good-enough reason — that each autistic person has embraced a particular interest. Find that reason, and you will find them, hiding in there, and maybe get a glimpse of their underlying capacities. In our experience, we found that showing authentic interest will help them feel dignity and impel them to show you more, complete with maps and navigational tools that may help to guide their development, their growth. Revealed capability, in turn, may lead to a better understanding of what's possible in the lives of many people who are challenged.

As the Disney Club members now say, it's about "finding the hidden ears."

Owen and I are driving to Griffin's office in the summer of 2012 for a rare visit. Owen hasn't seen Griffin since Christmas break. As we drive, Owen says, let's do "that love business." Lately we've been doing this at least once a day.

"O.K., you do Merlin," I say, which means I can do the young Arthur from Disney's 1962 "The Sword and the Stone." Arthur, thankfully, has only one line.

"You know, lad, this love business is

a powerful thing," he says in Merlin's reedy, old man's voice.

"Greater than gravity?" I respond as Arthur.

"Well, yes, boy, in its way." Owen pauses, considering it all, just as the wizard does in this, one of his favorite passages. "Yes, I'd say it's the greatest force on earth."

Romantic love. It's running through him, first and fresh, which is what he tells Griffin as they sit in the office. "I've fallen in love with a wonderful, kind, beautiful, soft and gentle girl, who likes the same things I like — animated movies, mostly hand-drawn, and mostly from Disney."

Griffin is giddy. He wants to know everything about Emily, Owen's girlfriend. He lays it all out: the tale of how they met at Riverview, how she's in Disney Club, their first kiss.

For most of us, social interactions don't feel so much like work. We engage instinctively, with sensations and often satisfactions freely harvested in the search itself. For Owen, much of that remains hard work. Despite his often saying to Griffin that his aim is to be popular — a catchall for the joys of connecting with other people — that goal, largely theoretical, has been like watery fuel in his sputtering engine.

Now, it's high-octane. That's what a first kiss can do. The specific therapeutic yield of this awakening is an intense focus, at long last, on social engagement — but at its very highest peak: the mysteries of how two people can be like one.

Owen tells Griffin that Aladdin and Jasmine have been helpful. "I need to give her space," he says of Emily. "That's what Aladdin learns. Jasmine needs to make the choices for herself. She has to choose, and he needs to know what she wants."

Griffin presses forward on his chair, his face close to Owen's. "But how can you know what she wants?"

Owen nods immediately. He's on it. "I have a song." He explains it is from a movie called "Quest for Camelot," an Arthurian romance a few Disney expats worked on for Warner Brothers in 1998. "The song is called 'Looking Through Your Eyes.'" He explains that he listens to the song every morning "to make sure I don't forget to see the world through her eyes."

For nearly a decade, Owen has been coming to see Griffin in this basement office, trying to decipher the subtle patterns of how people grow close to one another. That desire to connect has always been there as, the latest research indicates, it may be in all autistic people; their neurological barriers don't kill the desire, even if it's deeply submerged. And this is the way he still is — autism isn't a spell that has been broken; it's a way of being.

That means the world will continue to be inhospitable to him, walking about, as he does, uncertain, missing cues, his heart exposed. But he has desperately wanted to connect, to feel his life, fully, and — using his movies and the improvised tool kit we helped him build — he's finding his footing. For so many years, it was about us finding him, a search joined by Griffin and others. Now it was about him finding himself.

"Owen, my good friend," Griffin says, his eyes glistening, "it's fair to say, you're on your way."

Owen stands up, that little curly-haired boy now a man, almost Griffin's height, and smiles, a knowing smile of self-awareness.

"Thank you, Rafiki," Owen says to Griffin. "For everything."

"Is friendship forever?" Owen asks me.

"Yes, Owen, it often is."

"But not always."

"No, not always."

It's later that night, and we're driving down Connecticut Avenue after seeing the latest from Disney (and Pixar), "Brave." I think I understand now, from a deeper place, how Owen, and some of his Disney Club friends, use the movies and why it feels so improbable.

Most of us grow from a different direction, starting as utterly experiential, sorting through the blooming and buzzing confusion to learn this feels good, that not so much, this works, that

Owen, 12, playing a song from a Disney movie for his grandfather's birthday in 2003.

Owen, at age 20, in the bedroom of his apartment, where he is living on his own for the first time.

doesn't, as we gradually form a set of rules that we live by, with moral judgments at the peak.

Owen, with his reliance from an early age on myth and fable, each carrying the clarity of black and white, good and evil, inverts this pyramid. He starts with the moral — beauty lies within, be true to yourself, love conquers all — and tests them in a world colored by shades of gray.

It's the sidekicks who help him navigate that eternal debate, as they often do for the heroes in their movies. "I know love lasts forever!" Owen says after a few minutes.

We're approaching Chevy Chase Circle, five minutes from where we live. I know I need to touch, gently, upon the notion that making friends or finding love entails risk. There's no guarantee of forever. There may be heartbreak. But we do it anyway. I drop this bitter morsel into the mix, folding around it an affirmation that he took a risk when he went to an unfamiliar place on Cape Cod, far from his friends and home, and found love. The lesson, I begin, is "to never be afraid to reach out."

He cuts me off. "I know, I know," he says, and then summons a voice for support. It's Laverne, the gargoyle from "The Hunchback of Notre Dame."

"Quasi," he says. "Take it from an old spectator. Life's not a spectator sport. If watchin's all you're gonna do, then you're gonna watch your life go by without you."

He giggles under his breath, then does a little shoulder roll, something he does when a jolt of emotion runs through him. "You know, they're not like the other sidekicks."

He has jumped ahead of me again. I scramble. "No? How?"

"All the other sidekicks live within their movies as characters, walk around, do things. The gargoyles only live when Quasimodo is alone with them."

"And why's that?"

"Because he breathes life into them. They only live in his imagination."

Everything is still. "What's that mean, buddy?"

He purses his lips and smiles, chin out, as if he got caught in a game of chess. But maybe he wanted to. "It means the answers are inside of him," he says.

"Then why did he need the gargoyles?"

"He needed to breathe life into them so he could talk to himself. It's the only way he could find out who he was."

"You know anyone else like that?"

"Me." He laughs a sweet, little laugh, soft and deep. And then there's a long pause.

"But it can get so lonely, talking to yourself," my son Owen finally says. "You have to live in the world." ●

The New York Times
Understanding Autism

Special thanks: Brad Beatson, Melissa Frankenberry, Samantha Lebofsky, Kate Roncinske, Laura Villano

PHOTO CREDITS

Front Cover Andreas Samuelsson © 2020 Andreas Samuelsson. Distributed by The New York Times Licensing Group **Back Cover** Travis Huggett

Page 1: Cayce Clifford for The New York Times **Page 3:** Aspiritech and ZR Images

Introduction Pages 4-5: Fred R. Conrad/The New York Times **Page 7:** Pictorial Press Ltd./Alamy

Child and Family Page 9: Andreas Samuelsson © 2020 Andreas Samuelsson. Distributed by The New York Times Licensing Group **Pages 10-14:** Travis Huggett (4) **Page 15:** Kathleen O'Brien/The New York Times **Pages 17-18:** Courtesy Jen Malia (2) **Pages 20-21:** Mark Smith/Theispot **Page 23:** Scott Laumann/Theispot **Page 24:** Giselle Potter **Pages 27-31:** Erin Lefevre (10)

Autism and Science Page 33: Andreas Samuelsson © 2020 Andreas Samuelsson. Distributed by The New York Times Licensing Group **Page 35:** CokaPoka/Shutterstock **Page 37** (from left): Courtesy Daifeng Wang & Mark Gerstein, Yale University; Alfred Pasieka/Science Source **Page 38:** Courtesy Dr. John Constantino **Page 41:** jgaunion/iStockphoto/Getty Images **Page 43:** Valentyn Ogirenko/Reuters

Aiding the Autistic Page 45: Andreas Samuelsson © 2020 Andreas Samuelsson. Distributed by The New York Times Licensing Group **Pages 47-49:** Ryan Pfluger/AUGUST (2) **Page 50:** Calla Kessler/The New York Times **Pages 52-54:** Joshua Bright for The New York Times (2) **Page 56:** Courtesy of the Thibault Family **Pages 59-60:** Cayce Clifford for The New York Times (2) **Page 61:** Michelle Gustafson for The New York Times **Page 62:** Joshua Bright for The New York Times **Pages 64-65:** Aaron Limoges **Pages 66-67:** Allen J. Schaben/Los Angeles Times via Getty Images **Pages 68-69:** Erik Eiser/A Walk On Water **Pages 70-71:** Desiree Rios/The New York Times

Autism in Our Culture Page 73: Andreas Samuelsson © 2020 Andreas Samuelsson. Distributed by The New York Times Licensing Group **Pages 74-75:** The cast of the Indiana Repertory Theatre's 2017 production of The Curious Incident of the Dog in the Night-Time. Photo by Zach Rosing. **Page 76:** Shane Lavalette for The New York Times **Page 78:** Giselle Potter **Page 80:** Allison Filice **Page 83** (from top): Adrian Mangel; no credit **Pages 85-93:** From the Suskind family (6) **Page 94:** © The Orchard/Courtesy Everett Collection **Page 96:** Fred R. Conrad/The New York Times

A Peek Inside

As a high school student, Justin Canha, now 29 years old, filled this notebook with a multitude of characters that he loved to draw. For Justin, who is autistic, the notebook was at once a therapeutic and fun way to express himself.

Made in the USA
Columbia, SC
09 June 2020

10521003R00055